Anatomy
1800 Multiple Choice Questions

ANATOMY 1800 Multiple Choice Questions

M J T FitzGerald, MD, PhD, DSc

Professor and Chairman, Department of Anatomy, University College, Galway, Ireland;
Formerly Associate Professor, Department of Biological Structure, University of Washington School of Medicine, Seattle, USA

James P Golden, MB, FRCSI

Chief of Surgery, County Hospital, Co. Donegal, Ireland

Maeve FitzGerald, MB, BCh, BSc

Senior Lecturer, Department of Anatomy, University College, Galway, Ireland;
Formerly of the Department of Oral Biology, University of Washington School of Dentistry and Department of Anatomy, St Louis University School of Medicine, Missouri, USA

Butterworths
London Boston Durban Singapore Sydney Toronto Wellington

First published 1973
Reprinted 1975
Reprinted 1977
Reprinted 1978
Reprinted 1981
Reprinted 1984
Revised Edition 1986

© Butterworth & Co. (Publishers) Ltd, 1986

British Library Cataloguing in Publication Data

FitzGerald, M. J. T.
   Anatomy : 1800 multiple choice questions.—Rev. ed.
   1. Anatomy, Human—Problems, exercises, etc.
   I. Title   II. Golden, James P.   III. FitzGerald, Maeve
   611'.0076   QM32

ISBN 0-407-00341-X

Library of Congress Cataloging in Publication Data

FitzGerald, M. J. T.
   Anatomy : 1800 multiple choice questions.
   1. Anatomy, Human—Examinations, questions, etc.
   I. Golden, James P.   II. FitzGerald, Maeve
   [DNLM: 1. Anatomy—examination questions.
   QS 18 F554a]
   QM32.F57   1986   611'.0076   85-26902

ISBN 0-407-00341-X

Photoset by Butterworths Litho Preparation Department
Printed and bound in England by Anchor Brendon Ltd.,
Tiptree, Essex

07 298

PREFACE

This book supersedes *Anatomy: 1600 Multiple Choice Questions*, published by Butterworths in 1973. In addition to being longer, it differs from that book in the following respects: many of the Gross Anatomy questions have been revised or substituted; the Histology section has been substantially enlarged, and segregated from the Gross Anatomy; Embryology has also been segregated; Neuroanatomy has been updated; and an entirely new and larger set of illustrations is provided.

MJTF
JPG
MF

INSTRUCTIONS FOR STUDENTS

The various sections of the book should be used upon completion of the corresponding parts of your Anatomy course.

In assessing your own performance on a particular section you should bear in mind that the questions fall into two categories for scoring purposes. In the 'group true-false' type of question you are required to judge whether each one of the five statements provided is true or false. In grading these answers it is common practice to award a mark for each correct decision, and to deduct a mark for each wrong decision. The average score obtained by chance alone will therefore be zero.

The remaining questions belong to the second category, in which you are required to make a selection from a number of answers provided. A score of 20–25 per cent is to be expected on the basis of chance.

Note on Section VIII: Histology
In this Section, the questions in each of the six standard formats are arranged in the same sequence, as follows: the Cell; the Tissues (commencing with the Epithelia and ending with Nervous Tissue); and the Systems (commencing with the Cardiovascular and ending with the Reproductive). *Having studied a particular topic, the student should attempt the relevant questions within each format.*

CONTENTS

I UPPER LIMB

Questions 1–39

For each of the following multiple choice questions select the *one* most appropriate answer:

1. The spine of the scapula is continued laterally as the:
    A   Coracoid porcess
    B   Angle of the scapula
    C   Infraglenoid tubercle
    D   Supraglenoid tubercle
    E   Acromion process

2. Muscle attached to the coracoid process of scapula:
    A   Biceps
    B   Triceps
    C   Pectoralis major
    D   Deltoid
    E   Serratus anterior

3. Vein which pierces the clavipectoral fascia:
    A   Basilic
    B   Lateral pectoral
    C   Internal thoracic
    D   Axillary
    E   Cephalic

1

4. **The axillary vein:**
   A   Is lateral to the axillary artery
   B   Is devoid of valves
   C   Lies anterior to pectoralis minor
   D   Is directly continuous with the brachiocephalic vein
   E   None of the above

5. **Branch of the axillary artery:**
   A   Suprascapular
   B   Transverse cervical
   C   Lateral thoracic
   D   Nutrient artery to humerus
   E   Internal thoracic

6. **Origin from lateral cord of brachial plexus:**
   A   Axillary nerve
   B   Ulnar nerve
   C   Lateral cutaneous nerve of forearm
   D   Musculocutaneous nerve
   E   Suprascapular nerve

7. **The humerus may be rotated laterally by:**
   A   Subscapularis
   B   Supraspinatus
   C   Pectoralis major
   D   Deltoid
   E   None of the above

8. **The muscle pair responsible for abducting the humerus to a right angle:**
   A   Deltoid and subscapularis
   B   Deltoid and supraspinatus
   C   Supraspinatus and subscapularis
   D   Teres major and subscapularis
   E   Deltoid and teres major

9. **Abduction of the humerus is initiated by:**
   A Supraspinatus
   B Infraspinatus
   C Deltoid
   D Pectoralis minor
   E Trapezius

10. **The muscle pair which assists in elevating the arm above the head:**
    A Trapezius and pectoralis minor
    B Levator scapulae and serratus anterior
    C Rhomboid major and serratus anterior
    D Rhomboid major and levator scapulae
    E Trapezius and serratus anterior

11. **Muscle(s) supplied by the axillary nerve:**
    A Latissimus dorsi
    B Deltoid
    C Infraspinatus
    D Teres major
    E All of the above

12. **The shoulder joint is weakest:**
    A Above
    B Below
    C In front
    D Behind
    E Laterally

13. **Nerve(s) supplying shoulder joint:**
    A Radial
    B Lateral pectoral
    C Axillary
    D Suprascapular
    E All of the above

14. **The nerve trunk most intimately related to the capsule of the shoulder joint is:**
    A Radial
    B Axillary
    C Median
    D Ulnar
    E Musculocutaneous

15. **The following muscles belong to the 'rotator cuff' group** *except:*
    A Subscapularis
    B Deltoid
    C Supraspinatus
    D Infraspinatus
    E Teres minor

16. **Muscles having an intracapsular tendon:**
    A Long head of biceps
    B Short head of biceps
    C Coracobrachialis
    D Long head of triceps
    E None of the above

17. **In contact with medial wall of axilla:**
    A Medial root of median nerve
    B Medial cord of brachial plexus
    C Ulnar nerve
    D Medial pectoral nerve
    E Nerve to serratus anterior

18. **Muscle inserted into medial lip of intertubercular sulcus:**
    A Teres major
    B Teres minor
    C Pectoralis major
    D Pectoralis minor
    E Latissimus dorsi

19. **The apex of the cubital fossa is formed by:**
    A   Brachioradialis and pronator teres
    B   Brachialis and pronator teres
    C   Brachioradialis and biceps brachii
    D   Biceps brachii and supinator
    E   Brachioradialis and supinator

20. **The lateral cutaneous nerve of the forearm is derived from the — nerve:**
    A   Musculocutaneous
    B   Median
    C   Ulnar
    D   Radial
    E   Axillary

21. **Usual level of bifurcation of the brachial artery:**
    A   Middle of arm
    B   Just above the elbow
    C   Level of intercondylar line
    D   Level of elbow joint line
    E   Neck of radius

22. **An important supinator muscle:**
    A   Biceps brachii
    B   Brachialis
    C   Triceps
    D   Brachioradialis
    E   Flexor carpi radialis

23. **Supplied by the ulnar nerve in the forearm:**
    A   Flexor carpi radialis
    B   Flexor carpi ulnaris
    C   Extensor carpi radialis
    D   Extensor carpi ulnaris
    E   Flexor pollicis longus

24. **Tendon directly medial to dorsal (Lister's) tubercle of radius:**
    A   Extensor pollicis brevis
    B   Extensor pollicis longus
    C   Extensor indicis
    D   Extensor carpi radialis longus
    E   Extensor carpi radialis brevis

25. **Directly behind palmaris longus at the wrist:**
    A   Flexor carpi radialis
    B   Flexor pollicis longus
    C   Ulnar artery
    D   Radial artery
    E   Median nerve

26. **The carpal bones articulating with the radius are:**
    A   Scaphoid and pisiform
    B   Lunate and pisiform
    C   Lunate and trapezium
    D   Lunate and scaphoid
    E   Scaphoid and capitate

27. **The triangular fibrocartilage:**
    A   Is attached to styloid process of radius
    B   Separates synovial cavities of radiocarpal and inferior radio-ulnar joint
    C   Articulates with lunate bone when wrist is adducted
    D   Is stationary during pronation and supination
    E   Is commonly absent

28. **Artery usually palpable in the floor of the 'anatomical snuff box':**
    A   Princeps pollicis
    B   Radialis pollicis
    C   Radialis indicis
    D   Radial
    E   Palmar branch of radial

29. **Liable to dislocation in a heavy fall on the hand:**
   A Scaphoid
   B Lunate
   C Triquetral
   D Pisiform
   E Hamate

30. **Digital synovial sheath(s) in communication with ulnar bursa:**
   A Index
   B Middle finger
   C Ring finger
   D Little finger
   E All the above

31. **In the carpal tunnel:**
   A Ulnar nerve
   B Median nerve
   C Radial nerve
   D Ulnar artery
   E Radial artery

32. **Carpal bones visible in radiograph of newborn:**
   A None
   B Two
   C Four
   D Six
   E Eight

33. **Metacarpal bone with epiphysis at proximal end:**
   A First
   B Second
   C Third
   D Fourth
   E Fifth

34. **Abduction of the thumb carries it:**
   A Forwards away from the palm
   B Backwards to the side of the palm
   C Towards the index finger
   D Laterally, away from the index finger
   E In a direction intermediate between A and D

35. **Number of muscles inserted on index finger:**
    A Three
    B Four
    C Five
    D Six
    E Seven

36. **In the hand, the median nerve supplies:**
    A Abductor pollicis brevis
    B Adductor pollicis
    C First palmar interosseous
    D Abductor pollicis longus
    E Extensor indicis

37. **The innervation of the lumbrical muscles is related to the innervation of:**
    A Flexor digitorum superficialis
    B Flexor digitorum profundus
    C Extensor digitorum
    D The interossei
    E The two flexor carpi muscles

38. **The skin of the index finger is supplied by:**
    A Ulnar and radial nerves
    B Radial and median nerves
    C Median and ulnar nerves
    D Median only
    E Radial only

39. **The skin of the palm is supplied by:**
    A Ulnar and median nerves
    B Radial and median nerves
    C Radial and ulnar nerves
    D Ulnar nerve alone
    E Radial nerve alone

Questions 40–61

The set of lettered headings below is followed by a list of
numbered words or phrases. For each numbered word or phrase
select the correct answer under:

A   If the item is associated with A only
B   If the item is associated with B only
C   If the item is associated with both A and B
D   If the item is associated with neither A nor B

A   Deltoid
B   Trapezius
C   Both
D   Neither

40.   Attached to spine of scapula *B*
41.   Can elevate the shoulder
42.   Supplied by the axillary nerve
43.   Can retract the scapula

A   Supinator of forearm
B   Flexor of elbow
C   Both
D   Neither

44.   Biceps brachii
45.   Triceps brachii
46.   Pronator teres
47.   Brachialis
48.   Coracobrachialis

A   Biceps
B   Brachialis
C   Both
D   Neither

49.   Origin from humerus *B*
50.   Insertion into radius
51.   Blood supply from brachial artery
52.   Motor supply from median nerve

A   Anterior interosseous nerve
B   Posterior interosseous nerve
C   Both
D   Neither

53. Pierces supinator muscle
54. Derived from ulnar nerve
55. Sensory to wrist joint
56. Extensive cutaneous distribution

A   Flexor of wrist
B   Flexor of index finger
C   Both
D   Neither

57. Flexor carpi radialis
58. Flexor carpi ulnaris
59. Flexor digitorum superficialis
60. Flexor digitorum profundus
61. Palmaris longus

Questions 62–79

Directions: In the following series of questions, one or more of the four items is/are correct.

Answer   A   if 1, 2 and 3 are correct
         B   if 1 and 3 are correct
         C   if 2 and 4 are correct
         D   if only 4 is correct
and   E   if all four are correct

62. **Muscles arising from the clavicle include:**
    1. Pectoralis major
    2. Trapezius
    3. Deltoid
    4. Subclavius

63. **The weight of the upper limb is transmitted to the trunk via the:**
   1. Trapezius muscle
   2. Coracoclavicular ligaments
   3. Clavicle
   4. Deltoid muscle

64. **Division of the long thoracic nerve is manifested by:**
   1. Inability to retract the scapula
   2. Wasting of the pectoralis major muscle
   3. Weakness of humeral adduction
   4. 'Winging' of the scapula

65. **Bursa(e) in communication with the shoulder joint synovial cavity:**
   1. Subacromial
   2. Supraspinatus
   3. Infraspinatus
   4. Subscapular

66. **Origin from medial epicondyle of humerus:**
   1. Flexor carpi radialis
   2. Palmaris longus
   3. Pronator teres
   4. Flexor carpi ulnaris

67. **Hinge joint(s):**
   1. Humero-ulnar
   2. Metacarpophalangeal
   3. Interphalangeal
   4. Wrist

68. **The flexor carpi radialis muscle:**
   1. Is a flexor of the wrist
   2. Is an abductor of the wrist
   3. Is supplied by the median nerve
   4. Grooves the trapezoid bone

69. **Brachioradialis muscle:**
    1. Arises from lateral supracondylar line
    2. Inserts into distal end of radius
    3. Is a flexor of elbow joint
    4. Is supplied by the median nerve

70. **The posterior interosseous nerve:**
    1. Passes between the radius and ulna
    2. Lies on the interosseous membrane throughout its course
    3. Is cutaneous to the back of the hand
    4. Supplies the extensor digitorum muscle

71. **The ulnar nerve usually supplies:**
    1. The medial half of flexor digitorum superficialis
    2. The lumbrical to the little finger
    3. The abductor pollicis brevis
    4. The first dorsal interosseous muscle

72. **Joint(s) containing intra-articular fibrocartilage:**
    1. Sternoclavicular
    2. Temporomandibular
    3. Acromioclavicular
    4. First carpometacarpal

73. **Muscle(s) supplied by anterior interosseous nerve:**
    1. Flexor digitorum profundus
    2. Flexor pollicis longus
    3. Pronator quadratus
    4. Pronator teres

74. **Bony attachment(s) of the flexor retinaculum:**
    1. Scaphoid
    2. Trapezium
    3. Hamate
    4. Pisiform

75. **Give(s) arterial contribution to deep palmar arch:**
    1. Main radial artery
    2. Main ulnar artery
    3. Deep branch of ulnar artery
    4. Superficial branch of radial artery

76. **Muscles innervated by the median nerve include:**
    1. Palmaris brevis
    2. Opponens pollicis
    3. Adductor pollicis
    4. First lumbrical

77. **Extension of thumb is aided by:**
    1. First lumbrical
    2. First palmar interosseous
    3. First dorsal interosseous
    4. Abductor pollicis longus

78. **Articulates with the hamate bone:**
    1. Capitate
    2. Triquetral
    3. Fifth metacarpal
    4. Fourth metacarpal

79. **Interossei inserted into middle finger:**
    1. Second palmar
    2. Second dorsal
    3. Third palmar
    4. Third dorsal

Questions 80–104

The group of questions below consists of numbered headings, followed by a list of lettered words or phrases. For each heading select the *one* word or phrase which is most closely related to it. *Note:* Each choice may be used *only once.*

80.	Coracobrachialis	A	Flexion of humerus
81.	Supraspinatus	B	Lateral rotation of humerus
82.	Suscapularis		
83.	Pectoralis minor	C	Abduction of humerus
84.	Infraspinatus	D	Medial rotation of humerus
		E	None of the above

85.	Common interosseous artery	A	Subclavian
86.	Profunda brachii artery	B	Axillary
87.	Suprascapular artery	C	Brachial
88.	Radialis indicis artery	D	Ulnar
89.	Lateral thoracic artery	E	None of the above

90.	Trapezius	A	Musculocutaneous nerve
91.	Deltoid		
92.	Brachialis	B	Accessory nerve
93.	Supinator	C	Ulnar nerve
94.	Flexor carpi ulnaris	D	Axillary nerve
		E	None of the above

95.	Flexion of the elbow	A	Median nerve
96.	Abduction of the shoulder	B	Musculocutaneous nerve
97.	Extension of the elbow	C	Radial nerve
98.	Pronation of the forearm	D	Ulnar nerve
99.	Abduction of index finger	E	Axillary nerve

100. Flexion of wrist	A	Extensor digitorum and extensor digiti minimi
101. Extension of wrist		
102. Extension of fingers	B	Flexor carpi radialis and radial carpal extensors
103. Adduction of wrist		
104. Abduction of wrist	C	Flexor and extensor carpi ulnaris
	D	Radial and ulnar carpal extensors
	E	Flexor carpi radialis and flexor carpi ulnaris

Questions 105–159

In reply to the following questions indicate whether you think each statement is *True* or *False:*

The serratus anterior:
105. Arises by digitations from the lower eight ribs
106. Inserts into the axillary border of scapula
107. Acts synergistically with trapezius in abduction of arm to 90 degrees
108. Nerve supply from thoracodorsal nerve
109. Paralysis gives rise to the condition known as 'winged scapula'

The axillary nerve:
110. Is a branch of the posterior cord of the brachial plexus
111. Is closely related to the shoulder joint
112. Is a purely motor nerve
113. Is accompanied by the profunda brachii artery
114. Pierces coracobrachialis

The axillary artery:
115. Begins at the upper border of the clavicle
116. Terminates as it crosses the inferior border of pectoralis minor
117. Is contained in the axillary sheath
118. Has the median nerve anterior to its proximal third
119. Has the radial nerve behind its distal third

At the shoulder joint:
120. Bony surfaces permit considerable movement
121. Stability depends mainly on glenoidal labrum
122. Subscapularis bursa communicates with synovial cavity
123. Long head of triceps arises within joint
124. Head of humerus is entirely intracapsular

The biceps brachii:
125. Flexes both the shoulder and the elbow joints
126. Both supinates and pronates the forearm
127. Short head arises from clavicle
128. Tendon of long head is partially enclosed in synovial membrane
129. Is supplied by the median nerve

The radial nerve:
130. Arises from lateral cord of brachial plexus
131. Supplies brachioradialis
132. Divides below the elbow into muscular and cutaneous components
133. Innervates most of the dorsal skin of the hand
134. When injured, could cause 'wrist drop'

The ulnar nerve:
135. Arises from the medial cord of the brachial plexus
136. Supplies skin on medial side of arm and forearm
137. Passes behind medial epicondyle of humerus
138. Supplies the interossei
139. When injured, thenar muscles waste

The median nerve:
140. Arises directly from trunks of the brachial plexus
141. Crosses the axillary artery from lateral to medial side
142. Enters the forearm through pronator quadratus
143. Enters the hand by passing through carpal tunnel
144. When injured, gives rise to the condition known as 'claw hand'

The carpal tunnel:
145. Is a fibro-osseous tunnel formed by carpal bones and palmar aponeurosis
146. Contains the tendons of flexor digitorum superficialis
147. Contains both the radial and ulnar arteries
148. Compression of nerve in tunnel causes sensory loss in index finger (palmar surface)
149. Contains portion of ulnar bursa

The palmar aponeurosis:
150. Is attached to the skin of the palm by fibrous septa
151. Is attached distally to the fibrous flexor sheaths
152. Protects the underlying tendons
153. Receives tendon of palmaris longus
154. Apex is attached to flexor retinaculum

In the hand:
155. The first dorsal interosseous muscle abducts the index finger
156. Abduction of the thumb takes place in a forward direction
157. The radial nerve supplies no intrinsic muscles
158. The superficial palmar arch is superficial to the palmar aponeurosis
159. The ulnar nerve supplies adductor pollicis

Shoulder region

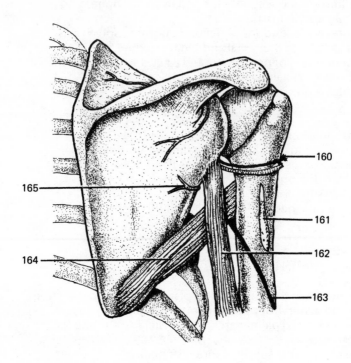

Identify the numbered structures, from the choices given below:

A   Axillary nerve
B   Circumflex scapular artery
C   Suprascapular artery
D   Radial nerve

E   Triceps, long head
F   Teres minor
G   Teres major
H   Triceps, lateral head

Section of arm

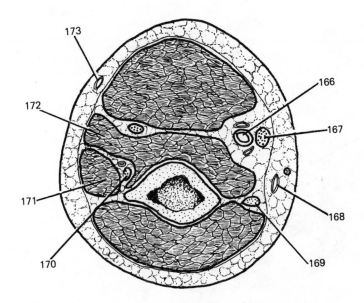

Identify the numbered structures, from the choices given below:

A	Median nerve	F	Brachioradialis
B	Cephalic vein	G	Basilic vein
C	Brachial artery	H	Biceps brachii
D	Brachialis	J	Triceps brachii
E	Radial nerve	K	Ulnar nerve

Section of wrist

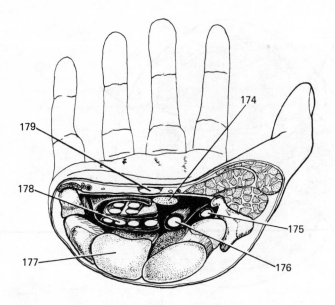

Identify the numbered structures, from the choices given below:

A Flexor carpi radialis
B Ulnar nerve
C Median nerve
D Palmaris longus

E Flexor pollicis longus
F Lunate bone
G Scaphoid bone
H Flexor digitorum
   profundus

Tendons at wrist

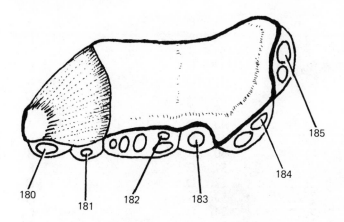

Identify the numbered structures, from the choices given below:

A Extensor carpi radialis
   brevis
B Extensor indicis
C Extensor pollicis longus
D Extensor digiti minimi

E Extensor carpi radialis
   longus
F Extensor digitorum
G Extensor carpi ulnaris
H Abductor pollicis
   longus

22

Answers

1. E	41. B	80. A
2. A	42. A	81. C
3. E	43. B	82. D
4. E	44. C	83. E
5. C	45. D	84. B
6. D	46. B	85. D
7. D	47. B	86. C
8. B	48. D	87. A
9. A	49. B	88. E
10. E	50. A	89. B
11. B	51. C	90. B
12. B	52. D	91. D
13. E	53. B	92. A
14. B	54. D	93. E
15. B	55. C	94. C
16. A	56. D	95. B
17. E	57. A	96. E
18. A	58. A	97. C
19. A	59. C	98. A
20. A	60. C	99. D
21. E	61. A	100. E
22. A		101. D
23. B		102. A
24. B	62. B	103. C
25. E	63. B	104. B
26. D	64. D	
27. B	65. D	105. F
28. D	66. E	106. F
29. B	67. B	107. F
30. D	68. A	108. F
31. B	69. A	109. T
32. A	70. C	110. T
33. A	71. C	111. T
34. A	72. A	112. F
35. E	73. A	113. F
36. A	74. E	114. F
37. B	75. B	115. F
38. B	76. C	116. F
39. A	77. D	117. T
	78. E	118. F
40. C	79. C	119. T

120. T	144. F	166. C
121. F	145. F	167. A
122. T	146. T	168. G
123. F	147. F	169. K
124. T	148. T	170. E
125. T	149. T	171. F
126. F	150. T	172. D
127. F	151. T	173. B
128. T	152. T	
129. F	153. T	
130. F	154. T	174. C
131. T	155. T	175. A
132. T	156. T	176. E
133. T	157. T	177. F
134. T	158. F	178. H
135. T	159. T	179. D
136. F		
137. T		
138. T	160. A	180. G
139. F	161. H	181. D
140. F	162. E	182. B
141. F	163. D	183. C
142. F	164. G	184. E
143. T	165. B	185. H

II LOWER LIMB

Questions 1–40

For each of the following multiple choice questions select the *one* most appropriate answer:

1. **The quadriceps femoris muscle:**
   A   Extends the knee
   B   Flexes the knee
   C   Extends the hip
   D   Rotates the knee
   E   Abducts the knee

2. **The femoral triangle is bounded by:**
   A   Inguinal ligament, pectineus, sartorius
   B   Inguinal ligament, adductor longus, gracilis
   C   Inguinal ligament, rectus femoris, sartorius
   D   Inguinal ligament, adductor longus, sartorius
   E   None of the above

3. **Immediately lateral to the lacunar ligament:**
   A   Femoral artery
   B   Femoral vein
   C   Femoral ring
   D   Femoral nerve
   E   Pectineus

4. **The femoral canal contains:**
   A   The femoral nerve
   B   The femoral artery
   C   The femoral vein
   D   The ilioinguinal nerve
   E   Lymphatics

5. **Artery in adductor canal:**
   A   Femoral
   B   Obturator
   C   Profunda femoris
   D   Perforating branch of profunda femoris
   E   Medial circumflex femoral

6. **The orifice in adductor magnus muscle transmits:**
   A   Femoral vessels
   B   Femoral nerve
   C   Saphenous nerve
   D   Tibial nerve
   E   Sciatic nerve

7. **A tributary of the long saphenous vein:**
   A   Short saphenous
   B   Sural
   C   Superficial epigastric
   D   Femoral
   E   Popliteal

8. **The greater sciatic foramen transmits the following structures, *except:***
   A   Superior gluteal vessels
   B   Posterior cutaneous nerve of thigh
   C   Piriformis muscle
   D   Obturator internus Lesser
   E   Inferior gluteal vessels

9.   The following muscles are inserted into the greater trochanter of femur, *except:*
     A   Gluteus maximus
     B   Gluteus medius
     C   Gluteus minimus
     D   Piriformis
     E   Obturator externus

10. Muscle pair inserted into iliotibial tract:
     A   Gluteus maximus and gluteus medius
     B   Gluteus medius and gluteus minimus
     C   Quadratus femoris and gluteus maximus
     D   Tensor fasciae latae and quadratus femoris
     E   Tensor fasciae latae and gluteus maximus

11. To avoid the sciatic nerve, an injection into the buttock is best given into:
     A   Upper and outer quadrant
     B   Upper and inner quadrant
     C   Lower and inner quadrant
     D   Lower and outer quadrant
     E   At the junction of the four quadrants

12. The sciatic nerve supplies the following muscles *except:*
     A   Biceps femoris:
     B   Semitendinosus
     C   Semimebranosus
     D   Gluteus maximus
     E   Adductor magnus

13. In the hip joint the synovial membrane does *not* line the:
     A   Inner surface of the capsule
     B   Ligament of the head of the femur
     C   Articular cartilages
     D   Non-articular surface of the femur
     E   Acetabular pad of fat

14. **Flexion of the hip joint is carried out by:**
    A   Iliopsoas —
    B   Vastus intermedius
    C   Semimebranosus
    D   Gluteus maximus
    E   Quadratus femoris

15. **Bony prominences on which you kneel:**
    A   Femoral condyles
    B   Patellae —
    C   Tibial condyles
    D   Intercondylar eminences of tibia
    E   Tibial tuberosities

16. **Muscle which flexes hip *and* knee:**
    A   Rectus femoris
    B   Semitendinosus
    C   Biceps femoris
    D   Sartorius
    E   Gracilis

17. **The structure closest to the posterior ligament of the knee joint:**
    A   Popliteal artery —
    B   Popliteal vein
    C   Tibial nerve
    D   Common peroneal nerve
    E   Sural nerve

18. **The following bursa always communicates with the knee joint synovial cavity:**
    A   Suprapatellar —
    B   Prepatellar
    C   Subcutaneous infrapatellar
    D   Deep infrapatellar
    E   Semimembranosus

28

19. **The saphenous nerve:**
    A   Is a branch of the obturator
    B   Gives a branch to the scrotum
    C   Is closely related to the great saphenous vein in the upper thigh   —
    D   Is cutaneous to the medial side of the foot
    E   Is motor to adductor magnus

20. **The cortex of the shaft of the tibia receives its main blood supply from:**
    A   Arteries in attached muscles
    B   The collateral circulation at knee and ankle
    C   The nutrient artery
    D   The circulus vasculosus
    E   None of the above

21. **The epiphysis of the upper end of tibia receives the attachment of:**
    A   Ligamentum patellae
    B   Fibular collateral ligament
    C   Sartorius
    D   Popliteus
    E   Gracilis

22. **The superficial peroneal nerve supplies:**
    A   Peroneus longus and brevis   —
    B   Peroneus tertius
    C   Tibialis anterior
    D   Extensor digitorum longus
    E   Flexor digitorum longus

23. **Articulates with head of talus:**
    A   Navicular   —
    B   Medial cuneiform
    C   Intermediate cuneiform
    D   Cuboid
    E   None of the above

24. **The following bones enter the medial longitudinal arch of the foot *except:***
   A   Talus
   B   Calcaneus
   C   Navicular
   D   Cuboid ⟶
   E   The three cuneiform bones

25. **Structure closest to the skin of the sole:**
   A   Flexor digitorum brevis
   B   Quadratus plantae
   C   Plantar aponeurosis ⟵
   D   Long plantar ligament
   E   Short plantar ligament

26. **Sesamoid bones in the foot are found in:**
   A   Flexor hallucis longus ⟵
   B   Flexor hallucis brevis
   C   Flexor digitorum longus
   D   Flexor digitorum brevis
   E   Quadratus plantae

27. **The talus provides origin for:**
   A   Extensor digitorum brevis
   B   Quadratus plantae
   C   Flexor hallucis longus
   D   Flexor digitorum brevis
   E   None of the above

28. **The medial plantar nerve:**
   A   Supplies cutaneous branches to 3½ toes ⟵
   B   Supplies motor branches to the interossei
   C   Supplies adductor hallucis
   D   Is homologous with the ulnar nerve in the hand
   E   Passes through the first intermetatarsal space

29. **The 'keystone' of the medial longitudinal arch of the foot is:**
    A   Head of talus
    B   Calcaneus
    C   Navicular
    D   Cuboid
    E   First metatarsal base

30. **The medial longitudinal arch of the foot is supported by:**
    A   Tibialis anterior
    B   Flexor hallucis longus
    C   The 'spring' ligament
    D   The plantar aponeurosis
    E   All of the above

31. **Inversion of the foot is performed by.:**
    A   Peroneus longus and brevis
    B   Peroneus longus and tibialis posterior
    C   Tibialis anterior and tibialis posterior
    D   Tibialis anterior and peroneus tertius
    E   None of the above muscle pairs

32. **The plantar nerves and vessels lie between:**
    A   Plantar aponeurosis and the first muscle layer
    B   First and second muscle layers
    C   Second and third muscle layers
    D   Third and fourth muscle layers
    E   Plantar aponeurosis and skin

33. **The cuboid is grooved by the tendon of:**
    A   Peroneus longus
    B   Peroneus brevis
    C   Peroneus tertius
    D   Tibialis posterior
    E   Flexor hallucis longus

34. **The ankle joint has greatest freedom of movement when:**
    A   It is plantar flexed
    B   It is dorsi-flexed
    C   The foot is inverted
    D   The foot is everted
    E   The forefoot is adducted

35. **The inverted posture of the newborn foot is due to:**
   A   Angulation of the neck of the talus
   B   Ligamentous shortening at the subtalar joint
   C   Contraction of tibialis anterior and posterior
        muscles
   D   Torsion at the talonavicular joint
   E   Late development of the Achilles tendon —

36. **The dorsalis pedis artery terminates by:**
   A   Dividing in the cleft between great and second toes
   B   Joining the deep plantar arch —
   C   Forming a dorsal arterial arch
   D   Dividing into medial and lateral plantar arteries
   E   Supplying the ankle joint

37. **Number of tarsal bones articulating with the five
    metatarsals:**
   A   Two
   B   Three
   C   Four —
   D   Five
   E   Seven

38. **The mid-tarsal joint:**
   A   Is between talus and calcaneus —
   B   Is between talus and navicular
   C   Comprises the talonavicular and calcaneo-cuboid
        joints
   D   Is a purely fibrous joint
   E   Permits dorsi-flexion of the foot

39. **The earliest epiphyseal centre of ossification to appear in the
    lower limb is for the:**
   A   Lower end of femur —
   B   Upper end of tibia
   C   Calcaneus
   D   Patella
   E   Head of fibula

40. **The following muscle of the hand has no homologue in the foot:**
    A   Abductor pollicis brevis
    B   Adductor pollicis
    C   Opponens pollicis
    D   First dorsal interosseous ⟵
    E   First lumbrical

Questions 41–76

The set of lettered headings below is followed by a list of numbered words or phrases. For each numbered word or phrase select the correct answer as follows:

A   If the item is associated with A only
B   If the item is associated with B only
C   If the item is associated with both A and B
D   If the item is associated with neither A nor B

A   Acetabulum
B   Head of femur
C   Both
D   Neither

41. Articulating surface devoid of hyaline cartilage
42. Ligament attached near centre
43. Joint capsule attached to margin
44. Centre of ossification appears in first postnatal year

A   Vastus medialis
B   Vastus lateralis
C   Both
D   Neither

45. Partial origin from hip bone
46. Partial origin from linea aspera
47. Muscular down to the level of the patella
48. Supplied only by femoral nerve

A   Extension of hip
B   Flexion of knee
C   Both
D   Neither

49. Sartorius
50. Semimembranosus
51. Gluteus maximus
52. Adductor magnus

A   Femoral artery
B   Femoral nerve
C   Both
D   Neither

53. Found in the femoral sheath
54. Medial to the femoral vein
55. Found in the femoral triangle
56. Normally palpable in the living

A   Long saphenous vein
B   Short saphenous vein
C   Both
D   Neither

57. Anterior to medial malleolus
58. Related to saphenous nerve at the ankle
59. Characterized by absence of valves
60. Perforating branches to deep veins of leg

A   Gluteus maximus
B   Gluteus medius
C   Both
D   Neither

61. Active in abduction of hip
62. Active in pelvic support when opposite limb is off the ground
63. Stabilizing action on the knee joint
64. Supplied by the superior gluteal nerve

A   Semitendinosus
B   Biceps femoris
C   Both
D   Neither

65. Origin exclusively from ischial tuberosity
66. Insertion into head of fibula
67. Medial rotator of flexed leg
68. Supplied by obturator nerve

A   Tibia
B   Fibula
C   Both
D   Neither

69. Articulation with lateral femoral condyle
70. Articulation with body of talus
71. Origin of tibialis anterior
72. Upper epiphysis appears before lower epiphysis

A   Medial plantar nerve
B   Lateral plantar nerve
C   Both
D   Neither

73. Derived from common peroneal nerve
74. Cutaneous to sole of foot
75. Motor to long flexor muscles
76. Motor to extensor digitorum brevis

Questions 77–90

Directions: In the following series of questions, one or more of
the four items is/are correct.

Answer A   if 1, 2 and 3 are correct
        B   if 1 and 3 are correct
        C   if 2 and 4 are correct
        D   if only 4 is correct
and   E   if all four are correct

77. **The ligament of the head of the femur:**
    1. Is attached to the margins of the acetabular notch
    2. Conveys blood vessels to the head of femur
    3. Is invested by synovial membrane
    4. Is sometimes absent

78. **Branches of lumbar plexus:**
    1. Sciatic nerve
    2. Obturator nerve
    3. Inferior gluteal nerve
    4. Lateral cutaneous nerve of thigh

79. **The right gluteus medius muscle:**
    1. Adducts the right femur
    2. Contracts when right foot bears body weight
    3. Inserts in lesser trochanter of femur
    4. Is supplied by superior gluteal nerve

80. **The biceps femoris muscle:**
    1. Has an origin from the ischial tuberosity
    2. Inserts into head of fibula
    3. Is a flexor of the knee joint
    4. Is a lateral rotator of the flexed knee joint

81. **The adductor tubercle:**
    1. Gives origin to the popliteus
    2. Receives the tendon of adductor magnus
    3. Gives attachment to the medial semilunar cartilage
    4. Is at the level of an epiphyseal plate

82. **Tibialis anterior:**
    1. Arises from the lateral surface of tibia
    2. Inserts into the medial surface of the medial cuneiform bone
    3. Passes beneath the extensor retinacula of the ankle
    4. Is invested by a synovial sheath at the ankle

83. **The gastrocnemius is:**
    1. Portion of the triceps surae
    2. Supplied by the tibial nerve
    3. A flexor of the knee
    4. A plantar flexor of the ankle

84. **The common peroneal nerve:**
    1. Supplies the long head of biceps femoris
    2. Forms the lateral plantar nerve
    3. Passes between tibia and fibula
    4. Is a branch of the sciatic nerve

85. **Compression of the common peroneal nerve at the neck of the fibula may produce:**
    1. Paralysis of eversion
    2. Paralysis of ankle dorsiflexion
    3. Anaesthesia on dorsum of foot
    4. Paralysis of plantar flexion

86. **Supplied by deep peroneal nerve:**
    1. Tibialis anterior
    2. Tibialis posterior
    3. Peroneus tertius
    4. Peroneus longus

87. **Bones articulating with the navicular:**
    1. Talus
    2. Intermediate cuneiform
    3. Lateral cuneiform
    4. Calcaneus

88. **The dorsalis pedis artery:**
    1. Is the continuation of the anterior tibial
    2. Is palpable between tibialis anterior and extensor hallucis longus tendons
    3. Passes between the first and second metatarsal bones
    4. Is the main blood supply to the sole of the foot

89. **The deltoid ligament is attached to the:**
    1. Medial malleolus
    2. Sustentaculum tali
    3. 'Spring' ligament
    4. Tubercle of the navicular

90. **Sesamoid bones are found in:**
    1. Peroneus longus
    2. Peroneus brevis
    3. Flexor hallucis brevis
    4. Flexor hallucis longus

Questions 91–108

The group of questions below consists of numbered headings, followed by a list of lettered words or phrases. For each heading select the *one* word or phrase which is most closely related to it. *Note:* Each choice may be used *only once.*

91.	Femoral artery	A	Inferior epigastric artery
92.	Popliteal artery		
93.	Profunda femoris artery	B	Superficial epigastric artery
94.	External iliac artery	C	Perforating arteries
		D	Paired genicular arteries

95.	Intertrochanteric line	A	Sacrotuberous ligament
96.	Ischial spine		
97.	Ischial tuberosity	B	Iliofemoral ligament
98.	Intertrochanteric crest	C	Sacrospinous ligament
99.	Pubic tubercle	D	Inguinal ligament
		E	None of the above

100.	Adductor magnus	A	Femoral nerve
101.	Biceps femoris	B	Obturator nerve
102.	Gracilis	C	Sciatic nerve
103.	Vastus intermedius	D	Superior gluteal nerve
104.	Tensor fasciae latae	E	Two of the above nerves

105.	Peroneus longus	A	Groove under
106.	Peroneus tertius		sustentaculum tali
107.	Flexor hallucis longus	B	Fifth metatarsal
108.	Tibialis posterior	C	Navicular
		D	Groove under cuboid

Questions 109–163

In reply to the following questions indicate whether you think each statement is *True* or *False*:

The hip joint:
109. Is a synovial, ball-and-socket joint
110. Is usually unstable at birth because ossification in the head of the femur has not commenced
111. Depends on muscular factors for its stability in the adult
112. Synovial cavity may communicate with bursa behind iliopsoas
113. Femoral neck fractures within the capsule may deprive the femoral head of its main blood supply

At the hip joint:
114. Ligamentum teres extends from pit on head to margins of acetabular notch
115. Iliopsoas is the principal flexor muscle
116. The obturator nerve supplies the knee as well as the hip
117. The hamstring muscles have an extensor function
118. The head of femur is mainly supplied by retinacular blood vessels

In the gluteal region:
119. The superior gluteal nerve supplies gluteus minimus
120. Gluteus medius muscle inserts into the lesser trochanter of the femur
121. The pudendal nerve leaves the buttock through the lesser sciatic foramen
122. The lesser sciatic foramen lies between the sacrotuberous and the sacrospinous ligaments
123. A branch of the inferior gluteal artery contributes to the cruciate anastomosis

Gluteus maximus:
124. Flexes the hip joint
125. Is attached to sacrotuberous ligament
126. Inserts entirely into gluteal ridge
127. Stabilizes flexed weight-bearing knee joint
128. Is supplied by the inferior gluteal nerve

The hamstring muscles:
129. Arise from ischial tuberosity
130. Insert into linea aspera
131. Receive blood from the profunda femoris artery
132. Are innervated by the sciatic nerve
133. Extend the hip joint during walking

The sciatic nerve:
134. Is formed entirely by sacral spinal nerves
135. Consists of two components, which pass through the greater and lesser sciatic foramina respectively
136. Passes midway between the greater trochanter and the ischial tuberosity
137. Rests on adductor magnus
138. Terminates by dividing into superficial and deep peroneal nerves

In the knee joint:
139. Synovial fluid can flow easily into the suprapatellar bursa
140. The medial meniscus is attached to the tibial collateral ligament
141. The lateral meniscus is not attached to the fibular collateral ligament
142. The cruciate ligaments prevent excessive movement of the tibia in an antero-posterior direction
143. Rotation is not permitted

Section of groin

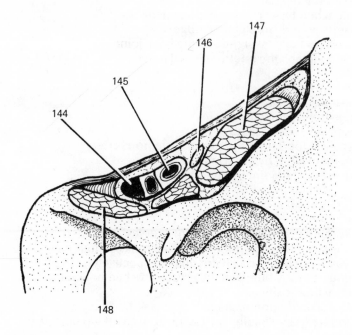

Identify the numbered structures, from the choices given below:

A   Femoral vein
B   Femoral nerve
C   Pectineus
D   Adductor longus

E   Femoral artery
F   Iliopsoas
G   Sartorius
H   Femoral ring

Gluteal region and thigh

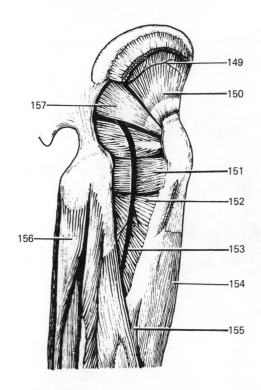

Identify the numbered structures, from the choices given below:

A	Quadratus femoris	F	Piriformis
B	Adductor magnus	G	Superior gluteal nerve
C	Biceps femoris	H	Inferior gluteal nerve
D	Gluteus minimus	J	Sciatic nerve
E	Vastus lateralis	K	Semitendinosus

Section of knee

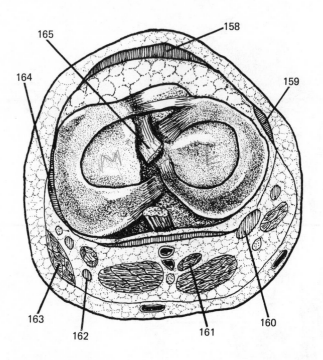

Identify the numbered structures, from the choices given below:

A   Fibular collateral
     ligament
B   Sartorius
C   Ligamentum patellae
D   Gracilis
E   Tibial collateral
     ligament

F   Iliotibial tract
G   Popliteus
H   Plantaris
J   Posterior cruciate
     ligament
K   Anterior cruciate
     ligament

Section of left leg

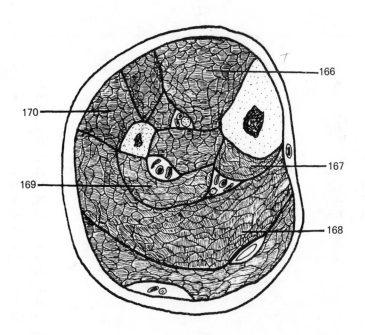

Identify the numbered structures, from the choices given below:

A	Peroneus longus	E	Flexor hallucis longus
B	Tibialis anterior	F	Peroneus brevis
C	Soleus	G	Tibialis posterior
D	Flexor digitorum longus	H	Extensor hallucis longus

44

Answers

1.	A	42.	B	83.	E
2.	D	43.	A	84.	D
3.	C	44.	B	85.	A
4.	E	45.	D	86.	B
5.	A	46.	C	87.	A
6.	A	47.	A	88.	B
7.	C	48.	C	89.	E
8.	D	49.	B	90.	B
9.	A	50.	C		
10.	E	51.	A	91.	B
11.	A	52.	A	92.	D
12.	D	53.	A	93.	C
13.	C	54.	D	94.	A
14.	A	55.	C	95.	B
15.	E	56.	A	96.	C
16.	D	57.	A	97.	A
17.	A	58.	A	98.	E
18.	A	59.	D	99.	D
19.	D	60.	C	100.	E
20.	C	61.	B	101.	C
21.	A	62.	B	102.	B
22.	A	63.	A	103.	A
23.	A	64.	B	104.	D
24.	D	65.	A	105.	D
25.	C	66.	B	106.	B
26.	B	67.	A	107.	A
27.	E	68.	D	108.	C
28.	A	69.	A		
29.	A	70.	C	109.	T
30.	E	71.	A	110.	T
31.	C	72.	A	111.	F
32.	B	73.	D	112.	T
33.	A	74.	C	113.	T
34.	A	75.	D	114.	T
35.	A	76.	D	115.	T
36.	B			116.	T
37.	C	77.	E	117.	T
38.	C	78.	C	118.	T
39.	A	79.	C	119.	T
40.	C	81.	E	120.	F
		81.	C	121.	T
41.	D	82.	E	122.	T

123. T	141. T	156. K
124. F	142. T	157. F
125. T	143. F	
126. F		158. C
127. T		159. A
128. T	144. H	160. G
129. T	145. E	161. H
130. F	146. B	162. D
131. T	147. F	163. B
132. T	148. C	164. E
133. T		165. K
134. F	149. G	
135. F	150. B	
136. T	151. A	166. B
137. T	152. D	167. G
138. F	153. J	168. C
139. T	154. E	169. E
140. T	155. C	170. A

III THORAX

Questions 1–16

For each of the following multiple choice questions select the *one* most appropriate answer:

1. **The sternum:**
    A   Is composed of four parts
    B   Gives origin to pectoralis minor
    C   Articulates with the upper ten costal cartilages
    D   Contains red marrow at its upper end only
    E   Makes a synovial joint with the clavicle

2. **The sternal angle is at the level of the lower border of vertebra:**
    A   T1
    B   T2
    C   T3
    D   T4
    E   T5

3. **The number of pairs of costal cartilages usually attached to the sternum:**
    A   Six
    B   Seven
    C   Eight
    D   Nine
    E   Ten

4. **The following ribs are typical *except* the:**
   A First
   B Third
   C Fifth
   D Seventh
   E Ninth

5. **The intercostal nerves and vessels course between:**
   A Skin and deep fascia
   B Deep fascia and external intercostals
   C External and internal intercostals
   D Internal and innermost intercostals
   E Innermost intercostals and endothoracic fascia

6. **The aortic arch lies behind:**
   A Manubrium sterni
   B Sternal angle
   C Body of sternum
   D Second right costal cartilage
   E Second left costal cartilage

7. **The most superficial structure in the superior mediastinum:**
   A Thymus
   B Arch of aorta
   C Left brachiocephalic vein
   D Brachiocephalic trunk
   E Vagus nerve

8. **The brachiocephalic trunk divides into two arteries:**
   A Right and left common carotid
   B Right common carotid and right subclavian
   C Left common carotid and left subclavian
   D Right and left subclavian
   E Right and left coronary

9. **The azygos vein:**
   A   Carries blood from the oesophagus
   B   Arches directly over the inferior lobe bronchus
   C   Passes between the vagus and the trachea
   D   Joins the superior vena cava behind the first costal cartilage
   E   None of the above

10. **The number of broncho-pulmonary segments in the middle lobe of the right lung is:**
    A   One
    B   Two
    C   Three
    D   Four
    E   From two to four

11. **Number of broncho-pulmonary segments in the right lower lobe of lung:**
    A   One
    B   Three
    C   Five
    D   Seven
    E   Nine

12. **The number of pulmonary veins entering the left atrium is normally:**
    A   One
    B   Two
    C   Four
    D   Six
    E   Eight

13. **The bundle of His usually receives its blood supply from the:**
    A   Right coronary artery
    B   Interventricular branch of the left coronary artery
    C   Right marginal artery
    D   Left marginal artery
    E   Left coronary trunk directly

14. **The following surface landmark is a guide to the gastro-oesophageal orifice:**
    - A   Seventh left costal cartilage
    - B   Left linea semilunaris
    - C   Tip of the ninth left costal cartilage
    - D   Xiphisternal joint
    - E   Left nipple

15. **Anterior to oesophagus:**
    - A   Left atrium
    - B   Left bronchus
    - C   Trachea
    - D   Lymph nodes
    - E   All of the above

16. **At the level of the sternal angle:**
    - A   Bifurcation of the pulmonary artery
    - B   Upper border of left atrium
    - C   Bifurcation of the trachea
    - D   Aortic valve
    - E   Formation of superior vena cava

Questions 17–35

The set of lettered headings below is followed by a list of numbered words or phrases. For each numbered word or phrase select the correct answer under:

- A   If the item is associated with A only
- B   If the item is associated with B only
- C   If the item is associated with both A and B
- D   If the item is associated with neither A nor B

A   Right lung
B   Left lung
C   Both
D   Neither

17. Attached by ligaments to chest wall
18. An oblique fissure is present
19. Impressed by azygos vein
20. Four broncho-pulmonary segments present in the upper lobe
21. Related to lower thoracic oesophagus

A   Right ventricle
B   Left ventricle
C   Both
D   Neither

22. Form(s) part of diaphragmatic surface of heart
23. Contain(s) the atrioventricular node in its wall
24. Frequently contains the septomarginal trabecula
25. Mitral valve guards its atrioventricular opening

A   Sinuatrial node
B   Atrioventricular node
C   Both
D   Neither

26. Composed of muscle fibres
27. Close to superior vena caval opening into right atrium
28. Initiates the heart beat
29. Receive(s) postganglionic fibres from the vagus
30. Gives rise to Purkinje fibres

A   Left coronary artery
B   Right coronary artery
C   Both
D   Neither

31. Origin from pulmonary artery
32. Main source of blood supply to bundle of His
33. Main blood supply to left ventricle
34. Innervated by the vagus
35. Origin from an aortic sinus

Questions 36–45

Directions: In the following series of questions, one or more of the four items is/are correct.

Answer A   if 1, 2 and 3 are correct
          B   if 1 and 3 are correct
          C   if 2 and 4 are correct
          D   if only 4 is correct
and   E   if all four are correct

36. **The mammary gland receives arterial supply from the:**
    1. Circumflex humeral
    2. Intercostal
    3. Subclavian
    4. Internal thoracic

37. **The lower aperture of the thorax is formed by the:**
    1. Lower costal cartilages
    2. Twelfth rib
    3. Xyphoid process
    4. Body of twelfth thoracic vertebra

38. **Synovial joint(s):**
    1. Sternoclavicular
    2. Manubriosternal
    3. Sternochondral
    4. Xiphisternal

39. **Accessory muscle(s) of inspiration:**
    1. Sternomastoid
    2. External oblique
    3. Pectoralis major
    4. Latissimus dorsi

40. **Among the contents of the mediastinum:**
    1. Trachea
    2. Lungs
    3. Phrenic nerves
    4. Diaphragm

41. **The following may impress the oesophagus during passage of barium swallow:**
    1.   Arch of aorta
    2.   Left bronchus
    3.   Left atrium
    4.   Left ventricle

42. **Of the two bronchi, the right is:**
    1.   Shorter
    2.   Wider
    3.   More vertical
    4.   In contact with the oesophagus

43. **Central tendon of diaphragm is pierced by:**
    1.   Aorta
    2.   Azygos vein
    3.   Oesophagus
    4.   Inferior vena cava

44. **The thoracic duct returns lymph from all areas of the body *except:***
    1.   Left half of the body below the diaphragm
    2.   Right half of the body below the diaphragm
    3.   Left half of the body above the diaphragm
    4.   Right half of the body above the diaphragm

45. **A three-inch stab wound passing radially through the left ninth intercostal space will pierce the:**
    1.   Spleen
    2.   Lung
    3.   Pleura
    4.   Kidney

Questions 46–94

In reply to the following questions indicate whether you think each statement is *True* or *False:*

At the lung root:
46. The left bronchus enters the lung before dividing
47. The hilar (bronchopulmonary) lymph nodes drain the entire lung
48. The bronchial arteries end in this region
49. One pulmonary vein emerges from each lung
50. The phrenic nerves descend posteriorly

The breast:
51. Is connected to skin and deep fascia by fibrous bands
52. Lymphatics drain entirely into the axilla
53. Frequently extends a 'tail' into the axilla
54. Left nipple is usually a little lower than right nipple
55. Accessory nipples may appear on the abdominal skin

The phrenic nerves:
56. Arise from the cervical plexus roots 3, 4, 5
57. Supply the skin over the deltoid muscles
58. Enter the thorax by crossing the necks of the first ribs
59. Give sensory branches to the mediastinal and diaphragmatic pleura
60. Are the only motor nerves to the diaphragm

The brachiocephalic veins:
61. Possess valves which prevent reverse blood flow during changes of intrathoracic pressure
62. Receive inferior thyroid veins
63. Lie in front of thymus when this is fully developed
64. In the infant, the left vein may encroach above the suprasternal notch
65. The right vein marks the right lung

The left vagus nerve:
66. Makes up part of the cranial parasympathetic outflow
67. Contributes to both the cardiac and pulmonary plexuses
68. Is in direct contact with the aortic arch
69. Injury in the region of the aortic arch may cause hoarseness
70. Enters the abdomen as the left gastric nerve

In the walls of the heart:
71. The left coronary artery divides into anterior interventricular and circumflex branches
72. The great cardiac vein accompanies the posterior interventricular artery
73. Parasympathetic ganglia are embedded in the atria
74. The coronary sinus occupies the atrioventricular groove
75. The septomarginal trabecula contains vagal nerve fibres

The right lung:
76. Auscultation of the middle lobe is best carried out immediately inferior to the scapula
77. The bronchus to the apical segment of the lower lobe is the first posterior branch of the bronchial tree
78. Expansion is brought about by muscles in the bronchial tree
79. Quiet expiration is a passive movement caused by elastic recoil of the lungs

The superior vena cava:
80. Lies behind the ascending aorta
81. Commences by the union of right internal jugular and subclavian veins
82. Receives the azygos vein
83. Is lodged in a groove in the upper lobe of the right lung
84. Is accompanied by the vagus nerve

The pericardium of the heart:
85. Is composed of outer serous and inner fibrous layers
86. The fibrous pericardium is attached to the inferior aspect of the right ventricle
87. Attachment to central tendon of diaphragm causes the heart to descend on inspiration
88. The layer on the surface of the heart is part of the epicardium
89. Visceral and parietal layers meet around the great vessels

The left atrium of the heart:
90. Receives one pulmonary vein on each side
91. Forms the anterior wall of the transverse sinus of the pericardium
92. Contains oxygenated blood in adult but not in fetal life
93. Has a bicuspid valve between it and the left ventricle
94. Is the most posterior heart chamber

Right lung

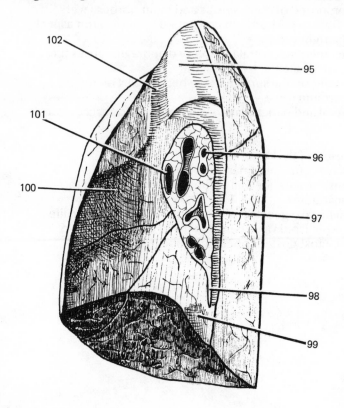

Identify the numbered structures, from the choices given below:

A   Trachea
B   Diaphragm
C   Right atrium
D   Azygos vein
E   Eparterial bronchus

F   Inferior vena cava
G   Pulmonary ligament
H   Pulmonary trunk
J   Anterior pulmonary vein
K   Superior vena cava

Mediastinum

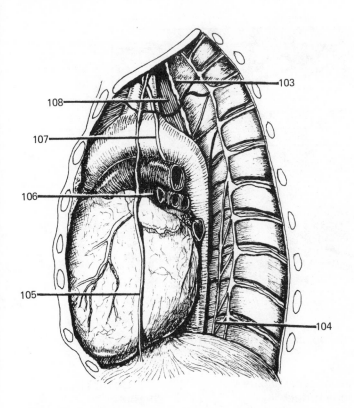

Identify the numbered structures, from the choices given below:

A   Phrenic nerve
B   Aortic arch
C   Vagus nerve
D   Thoracic duct

E   Greater splanchnic
     nerve
F   Oesophagus
G   Recurrent laryngeal
     nerve
H   Anterior pulmonary
     vein

Section of thorax

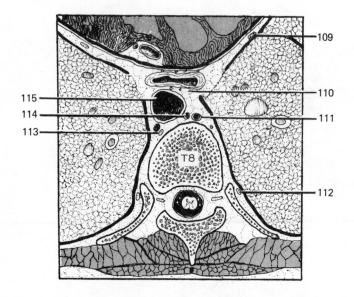

Identify the numbered structures, from the choices given below:

A   Oesophageal plexus
B   Thoracic duct
C   Recurrent laryngeal
    nerve
D   Azygos vein

E   Sympathetic chain
F   Phrenic nerve
G   Greater splanchnic
    nerve
H   Aorta

Answers

1.	E	39.	B	79.	T
2.	D	40.	B	80.	F
3.	B	41.	A	81.	F
4.	A	42.	A	82.	T
5.	D	43.	D	83.	T
6.	A	44.	D	84.	F
7.	A	45.	A	85.	F
8.	B			86.	F
9.	A	46.	T	87.	T
10.	B	47.	T	88.	T
11.	C	48.	F	89.	T
12.	C	49.	F	90.	F
13.	A	50.	F	91.	F
14.	A	51.	T	92.	F
15.	E	52.	F	93.	T
16.	C	53.	T	94.	T
		54.	T		
		55.	T		
17.	D	56.	T	95.	A
18.	C	57.	F	96.	E
19.	A	58.	F	97.	D
20.	D	59.	T	98.	G
21.	B	60.	T	99.	F
22.	C	61.	F	100.	C
23.	D	62.	T	101.	J
24.	A	63.	F	102.	K
25.	B	64.	T		
26.	C	65.	T	103.	D
27.	A	66.	T	104.	E
28.	A	67.	T	105.	A
29.	C	68.	T	106.	H
30.	B	69.	T	107.	C
31.	D	70.	F	108.	F
32.	B	71.	T		
33.	A	72.	F	109.	F
34.	D	73.	T	110.	A
35.	C	74.	T	111.	D
		75.	F	112.	E
36.	C	76.	F	113.	G
37.	E	77.	F	114.	B
38.	B	78.	F	115.	H

IV ABDOMEN

Questions 1–22

For each of the following multiple choice questions select the *one* most appropriate answer:

1. **Enclosed within the sheath of the rectus abdominis muscle:**
    A External oblique aponeurosis
    B Linea alba
    C Linea semilunaris
    D Transversalis fascia
    E None of the above

2. **The lower six intercostal nerves supply:**
    A Intercostal muscles only
    B Intercostal and abdominal muscles
    C Intercostal and abdominal muscles and overlying skin
    D All of the above structures, together with the subjacent parietal peritoneum
    E All of the above structures, together with both the parietal and visceral layers of the peritoneum

3. **The internal spermatic fascia is derived from the:**
    A External oblique
    B Internal oblique
    C Transversus abdominis
    D Transversalis fascia
    E Peritoneum

4. **Anterior to the deep inguinal ring:**
   A   Internal oblique
   B   Transversus abdominis
   C   Conjoint tendon
   D   Two of the above
   E   None of the above

5. **Immediately medial to the deep inguinal ring:**
   A   Femoral artery
   B   Linea alba
   C   Spermatic cord
   D   The inguinal (Hesselbach's) triangle
   E   Inferior epigastric artery

6. **Immediately anterior to the conjoint tendon:**
   A   Internal oblique
   B   Transversus abdominis
   C   Superficial inguinal ring
   D   Transversalis fascia
   E   None of the above

7. **Nerve passing through the superficial inguinal ring:**
   A   Iliohypogastric
   B   Ilioinguinal
   C   Lateral cutaneous of thigh
   D   Femoral
   E   Perineal

8. **The most common position of the vermiform appendix is:**
   A   Retrocaecal
   B   Retrocolic
   C   Retroileal
   D   Pelvic
   E   Subcaecal

9. **The mesentery of the appendix has an attachment to the:**
   A   Caecum
   B   Ascending colon
   C   Ileum
   D   Mesentery of ileum
   E   Posterior abdominal wall

10. **Upper boundary of the hepatorenal (right subhepatic) pouch:**
   A   Duodenum
   B   Right kidney
   C   Diaphragm
   D   Lower layer of coronary ligament
   E   Upper layer of coronary ligament

11. **The anterior limit of the normal spleen is represented by the:**
   A   Posterior axillary line
   B   Midaxillary line
   C   Anterior axillary line
   D   Mid-clavicular line
   E   Linea semilunaris

12. **Vertebral level of origin of renal arteries:**
   A   T12
   B   L1
   C   L2
   D   L3
   E   L4

13. **Vertebral level of bifurcation of abdominal aorta:**
   A   L2
   B   L3
   C   L4
   D   L5
   E   S1

14. **A branch of the hepatic artery:**
   A   Cystic
   B   Left gastric
   C   Splenic
   D   Gastrohepatic
   E   Oesophageal

15. **A branch of the inferior mesenteric artery:**
   A   Right colic
   B   Left colic
   C   Middle colic
   D   Left gastroepiploic
   E   Splenic

16. **Directly behind the duodenum:**
   A   Hepatic artery
   B   Gastroduodenal artery
   C   Right gastric artery
   D   Superior mesenteric vein
   E   Inferior mesenteric vein

17. **The left renal vein:**
   A   Is crossed anteriorly by the superior mesenteric artery
   B   Lies behind the left renal artery
   C   Joins the portal vein behind the pancreas
   D   Receives the inferior mesenteric vein
   E   None of the above

18. **The greater omentum is attached to:**
   A   Liver and stomach
   B   Stomach and jejunum
   C   Jejunum and colon
   D   Stomach and colon
   E   Liver and colon

19. **The following structures are found within the lesser omentum,** *except:*
   A   Hepatic artery
   B   Hepatic veins
   C   Common bile duct
   D   Lymphatics
   E   Vagal nerve fibres

20. **The superior mesenteric vessels:**
   A   Are the vessels of the primitive foregut
   B   Cross the third portion of duodenum
   C   Artery arises from aorta at L3 level
   D   Vein drains into the inferior vena cava
   E   All of the above

21. **The normal number of segments in the kidney is:**
    A   Three
    B   Five
    C   Seven
    D   Ten
    E   Twenty

22. **Behind the kidney:**
    A   Quadratus lumborum
    B   Twelfth rib
    C   Subcostal nerve
    D   Diaphragm
    E   All of the above

Questions 23–45

The set of lettered headings below is followed by a list of numbered words or phrases. For each numbered word or phrase select the correct answer under:

    A   If the item is associated with A only
    B   If the item is associated with B only
    C   If the item is associated with both A and B
    D   If the item is associated with neither A nor B

    A   Duodenum
    B   Jejunum
    C   Both
    D   Neither

23.   Site of Meckel's diverticulum
24.   Has a mesentery throughout entire length
25.   Arterial supply entirely from superior mesenteric
26.   Venous drainage to portal venous system

A   Jejunum
B   Ileum
C   Both
D   Neither

27. Myenteric (Auerbach's) plexus is lodged between muscle layers
28. Blood supply from superior mesenteric artery
29. Mesentery devoid of arterial arcades
30. Appendices epiploicae are a gross feature

A   Caecum
B   Appendix
C   Both
D   Neither

31. Taeniae coli present
32. A mesentery is present
33. Blood supply from superior mesenteric artery
34. Venous drainage to inferior vena cava
35. Unique to man

A   Liver
B   Spleen
C   Both
D   Neither

36. Attached to the diaphragm by peritoneal reflections
37. Venous drainage to inferior vena cava
38. Part of stomach bed
39. Arterial supply via coeliac artery
40. Invested by peritoneum of greater sac

A   Stomach
B   Spleen
C   Both
D   Neither

41. Supplied by branches of splenic artery
42. Gives attachment to gastrosplenic ligament
43. One surface is coated by peritoneum of lesser sac
44. Venous blood drains into portal venous system
45. In contact with left kidney

Questions 46–56

Directions: In the following series of questions, one or more of the four items is/are correct.

Answer A   if 1, 2 and 3 are correct
        B   if 1 and 3 are correct
        C   if 2 and 4 are correct
        D   if only 4 is correct
and   E   if all four are correct

46. **The rectus abdominis is:**
    1. Attached to the ninth and tenth ribs
    2. Marked in its upper half by tendinous intersections
    3. Surrounded by the rectus sheath throughout its length
    4. A flexor of the vertebral column

47. **The epiploic foramen is bounded by the:**
    1. Lesser omentum
    2. Inferior vena cava
    3. Duodenum
    4. Quadrate lobe of liver

48. **The portal triad contains the:**
    1. Portal vein
    2. Hepatic artery
    3. Bile duct
    4. Lymphatic duct

49. **The portal vein receives blood from the:**
    1. Stomach
    2. Liver
    3. Caecum
    4. Kidneys

50. **Branch(es) of splenic artery:**
    1. Left gastric
    2. Right gastric
    3. Right gastro-epiploic
    4. Short gastric

51. **Characteristic of large intestine:**
    1. Taeniae coli
    2. Appendices epiploicae
    3. Haustra coli
    4. Plicae circulares

52. **Part(s) of colon having a mesentery:**
    1. Ascending
    2. Transverse
    3. Descending
    4. Sigmoid

53. **Relations of the right kidney include:**
    1. Duodenum
    2. Colon
    3. Liver
    4. Quadratus lumborum

54. **The spleen makes contact with:**
    1. Stomach
    2. Left kidney
    3. Pancreas
    4. Colon

55. **Posterior relation(s) of the right kidney:**
    1. Psoas major
    2. Quadratus lumborum
    3. Diaphragm
    4. Transversus abdominis

56. **Belong(s) to the stomach bed:**
    1. Jejunum
    2. Pancreas
    3. Right kidney
    4. Left kidney

Questions 57–71

The group of questions below consists of numbered headings,
followed by a list of lettered words or phrases. For each heading
select the *one* word or phrase which is most closely related to it.
Note: Each choice may be used *only once.*

57.	External oblique	A	Tunica vaginalis
58.	Internal oblique	B	External spermatic
59.	Rectus abdominis		fascia
60.	Transversalis fascia	C	Internal spermatic
61.	Peritoneum		fascia
		D	Cremaster
		E	None of the above

62.	Body of gall bladder	A	Tail of pancreas
63.	Hilum of spleen	B	Second part of
64.	Hepatic flexure of		duodenum
	colon	C	First part of duodenum
65.	Quadrate lobe of liver	D	Right kidney
66.	Caudate lobe of liver	E	None of the above

67.	Left gastric vein	A	Inferior vena cava
68.	Inferior mesenteric	B	Renal vein
	vein	C	Portal vein
69.	Inferior epigastric vein	D	Splenic vein
70.	Left testicular vein	E	External iliac vein
71.	Right ovarian vein		

Questions 72–106

In reply to the following questions indicate whether you think
each statement is *True* or *False:*

The anterior abdominal wall:
72. Muscles contract during coughing
73. Is innervated mainly by lumbar nerves
74. Skin lymphatics above umbilicus drain to axillary nodes
75. Veins below umbilicus drain mainly into the portal system
76. Inferior attachment of membranous (Scarpa's) fascia is to
the inguinal ligament

The inguinal canal:
77. Contains the spermatic cord in the male but only fat in the female
78. Normally contains a peritoneal diverticulum in adults
79. Is more oblique in the adult than in the newborn
80. Its superficial ring is protected by the pyramidalis muscle
81. Is absent in the male if the testis is undescended

The portal vein:
82. Is formed by union of superior and inferior mesenteric veins
83. Carries venous blood from the spleen
84. Runs in the lesser omentum with a branch of the coeliac artery
85. Notches the bare area of the liver
86. Obstruction may be manifested by dilated paraumbilical veins

The spleen:
87. Is a highly vascular organ
88. Is related to both the greater and lesser sacs of peritoneum
89. Normally lies in the axis of the left tenth rib
90. In the adult is normally palpable below the left rib margin
91. Cannot be palpated in the infant

The duodenum:
92. Is retroperitoneal in its entire length
93. Is directly related to the right kidney
94. Lies anterior to the common bile duct
95. Lies posterior to the superior mesenteric vessels
96. Is an important site of portosystemic venous anastomosis

The caecum:
97. Is non-distensible because of its relatively rigid wall
98. Contains liquid faeces and gas
99. Has well-developed taeniae coli
100. Occupies right upper abdomen in fetal life
101. Invariably occupies the right iliac fossa after birth

The abdominal aorta:
102. Enters the abdomen behind the medial arcuate ligament
103. Normally gives origin directly to the splenic artery
104. Is crossed superficially by the left renal vein
105. Is related to many lymph nodes
106. Bifurcates at the level of the fifth lumbar vertebra

Posterior abdominal structures

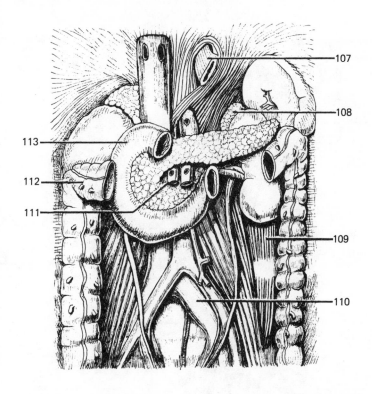

Identify the numbered structures, from the choices given below:

A   Duodenum
B   Suprarenal gland
C   Oesophagus
D   Common iliac artery
E   Common iliac vein

F   Splenic flexure of
     colon
G   Portal vein
H   Quadratus lumborum
J   Superior mesenteric
     vein
K   Hepatic flexure of
     colon

Nerves on posterior abdominal wall

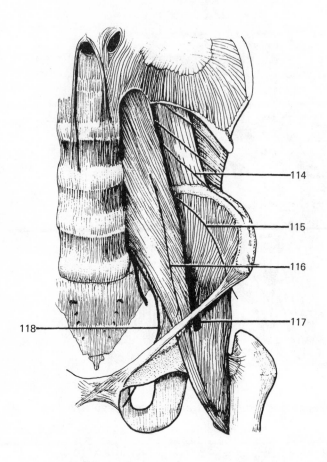

Identify the numbered structures, from the choices given below:

A   Gentiofemoral
B   Lumbosacral trunk
C   Ilioinguinal

D   Obturator
E   Lateral femoral
     cutaneous
F   Femoral

Answers

1.	E	42.	C	80.	F
2.	D	43.	A	81.	F
3.	D	44.	C	82.	F
4.	A	45.	B	83.	T
5.	E			84.	T
6.	C	46.	C	85.	F
7.	B	47.	A	86.	T
8.	A	48.	A	87.	T
9.	D	49.	B	88.	T
10.	D	50.	D	89.	T
11.	B	51.	A	90.	F
12.	C	52.	C	91.	F
13.	C	53.	E	92.	F
14.	A	54.	E	93.	T
15.	B	55.	E	94.	T
16.	B	56.	C	95.	T
17.	A			96.	F
18.	D			97.	F
19.	B	57.	B	98.	T
20.	B	58.	D	99.	T
21.	B	59.	E	100.	F
22.	E	60.	C	101.	F
		61.	A	102.	F
23.	D	62.	B	103.	F
24.	B	63.	A	104.	T
25.	B	64.	D	105.	T
26.	C	65.	C	106.	F
27.	C	66.	E		
28.	C	67.	C		
29.	D	68.	D	107.	C
30.	D	69.	E	108.	B
31.	A	70.	B	109.	H
32.	B	71.	A	110.	E
33.	C			111.	J
34.	D			112.	K
35.	D	72.	T	113.	A
36.	A	73.	F		
37.	A	74.	T		
38.	B	75.	F	114.	C
39.	C	76.	F	115.	E
40.	C	77.	F	116.	A
41.	C	78.	F	117.	F
		79.	F	118.	D

V PELVIS AND PERINEUM

Questions 1–15

For each of the following multiple choice questions select the *one* most appropriate answer:

1.   **The prostate:**
     A   Is the size of an orange
     B   Surrounds the membranous urethra
     C   Is pierced by the ductus (vas) deferens
     D   Has no function in man
     E   None of the above

2.   **The middle lobe of prostate is the part between:**
     A   Rectum and prostatic urethra
     B   Ejaculatory ducts and rectum
     C   Ejaculatory ducts and prostatic urethra
     D   Pubis and prostatic urethra
     E   Pubis and rectum

3.   **The ductus (vas) deferens is connected to the prostatic urethra by:**
     A   The prostatic utricle
     B   Gartner's duct
     C   The ejaculatory duct
     D   The urachus
     E   None of the above

4. **The anal valves are at the level of the:**
   A   Anorectal junction
   B   Anal margin
   C   White line of Hilton
   D   Rectal ampulla
   E   Pectinate line

5. **The uterine artery:**
   A   Usually arises from the internal iliac artery
   B   Anastomoses with the ovarian artery
   C   Crosses the ureter above the lateral vaginal fornix
   D   Gives branches to the vagina
   E   All of the above

6. **The internal os of the uterus marks the junction of:**
   A   Uterine tube and peritoneal cavity
   B   Uterine tube and fundus of uterus
   C   Fundus and body of uterus
   D   Body and cervix of uterus
   E   Cervix and vagina

7. **The lateral fornix of the vagina is most closely related to the:**
   A   Urethra
   B   Ureter
   C   Middle rectal artery
   D   Uterine artery
   E   Round ligament of uterus

8. **The following structures occupy the male superficial perineal pouch, *except:***
   A   Corpora cavernosa
   B   Corpus spongiosum
   C   Posterior scrotal nerves and vessels
   D   Bulbo-urethral glands
   E   Bulb of penis

9. **The inferior rectal nerve supplies:**
   A   External anal sphincter
   B   Internal anal sphincter
   C   Rectal mucous membrane
   D   Levator ani muscle
   E   Muscle of rectal ampulla

10. **The ischiorectal fossa is bounded directly by:**
   A   The rectum and ischium
   B   Obturator internus fascia and rectum
   C   Levator ani and obturator internus fascia
   D   Ischium and sacrum
   E   None of the above

11. **Location of sphincter urethrae:**
   A   Superficial perineal pouch
   B   Deep perineal pouch
   C   Ischiorectal fossa
   D   Above the prostate gland
   E   None of the above

12. **The internal iliac lymph nodes receive lymph from:**
   A   Body of uterus
   B   Cervix of uterus
   C   Prostate
   D   Rectum
   E   All of the above

13. **The superficial inguinal lymph nodes receive lymph from:**
   A   Anal canal
   B   Vagina
   C   Lower abdominal wall
   D   Rectum
   E   All of the above

14. **Nodes receiving lymph from the testis:**
   A   External iliac
   B   Internal iliac
   C   Superficial inguinal
   D   Presacral
   E   Para-aortic

15. **Composed of smooth muscle:**
    A Bulbospongiosus
    B Levator ani
    C Sphincter urethrae
    D External anal sphincter
    E Internal anal sphincter

Questions 16–40

The set of lettered headings below is followed by a list of numbered words or phrases. For each numbered word or phrase select the correct answer under:

A If the item is associated with A only
B If the item is associated with B only
C If the item is associated with both A and B
D If the item is associated with neither A nor B

A Prostate
B Bladder
C Both
D Neither

16. Lymph drainage to internal inguinal lymph nodes
17. Blood supply from inferior vesical artery
18. Pierced by ejaculatory ducts
19. Related to pelvic peritoneum
20. Contains the utricle

A Related behind to rectum
B Related in front to bladder
C Both
D Neither

21. Vagina
22. Seminal vesicle
23. Pouch of Douglas
24. Prostate
25. Cervix uteri

A   Levator ani
B   Sphincter ani externus
C   Both
D   Neither

26. Composed of striated muscle
27. Contains puborectalis
28. Partial origin from ischium
29. Motor supply from autonomic system
30. Attached to perineal body

A   Passes through greater sciatic notch
B   Passes through lesser sciatic notch
C   Passes through both
D   Passes through neither

31. Obturator externus
32. Obturator internus
33. Pudendal nerve
34. Sciatic nerve
35. Piriformis

A   Uterus
B   Ovary
C   Both
D   Neither

36. Lymph drainage to lumbar para-aortic nodes
37. Lymph drainage to internal iliac nodes
38. Venous drainage to internal iliac vein
39. Corpus luteum
40. Endometrium

Questions 41–46

Directions: In the following series of questions, one or more of
the four items is/are correct.
Answer A   if 1, 2 and 3 are correct
       B   if 1 and 3 are correct
       C   if 2 and 4 are correct
       D   if only 4 is correct
and   E   if all four are correct

41. **Male accessory sex gland(s):**
    1. Seminal vesicles
    2. Prostate
    3. Bulbo-urethral
    4. Testis

42. **Main source(s) of arterial supply to rectum:**
    1. Inferior rectal
    2. Middle rectal
    3. External iliac
    4. Superior rectal

43. **Site(s) of porto-systemic anastomosis:**
    1. Rectosigmoid junction
    2. Prostatic plexus
    3. Cervix uteri
    4. Anorectal junction

44. **The superior hypogastric plexus (presacral nerve) contains the following nerve fibres:**
    1. Preganglionic parasympathetic
    2. Preganglionic sympathetic
    3. Postganglionic parasympathetic
    4. Visceral afferent

45. **Stimulation of the pelvic splanchnic nerves will:**
    1. Empty the bladder
    2. Contract levator ani
    3. Cause erection of the penis
    4. Contract sphincter urethrae

46. **The female pelvis differs from the male pelvis in the following:**
    1. Greater transverse diameter
    2. Greater anteroposterior diameter
    3. Shallower pelvic cavity
    4. Wider subpubic angle

Questions 47–56

The group of questions below consists of numbered headings, followed by a list of lettered words or phrases. For each heading select the *one* word or phrase which is most closely related to it. *Note:* Each choice may be used *more than once.*

47.	Anal canal	A	Internal iliac nodes
48.	Body of uterus	B	Superficial inguinal
49.	Testis		nodes
50.	Bladder	C	Para-aortic nodes
51.	Vagina	D	Deep inguinal nodes
		E	None of the above

52.	Ischial tuberosity	A	Sacrotuberous
53.	Ischial spine		ligament
54.	Body of pubis	B	Sacrospinous ligament
55.	Conjoint ramus	C	Pubovesical ligament
56.	Pubic tubercle	D	Perineal membrane
		E	Inguinal ligament

Questions 57–91

In reply to the following questions indicate whether you think each statement is *True* or *False:*

The prostate gland:
57. Is situated in the perineum immediately below levator ani
58. Is surrounded by a plexus of veins
59. Has a stony hard consistency
60. Usually has a posterior median groove
61. Is palpable on rectal examination

The bladder:
62. Is an abdominal organ in the infant
63. Has peritoneum on its anterior surface when full
64. Has an entirely smooth-walled interior
65. Its muscular walls are pierced obliquely by the ureters
66. The urachus is a 'safety valve' allowing overflow when the urethra is obstructed.

The ovaries:
67. Are attached to the posterior leaf of the broad ligament of the uterus
68. Lie in the angle between the internal and external iliac arteries
69. Receive their blood supply from the internal iliac arteries
70. Are normally palpable on abdominal examination
71. Are attached to the broad ligaments by means of the ovarian ligaments

The vagina:
72. Surrounds the internal os of the uterus
73. Anterior wall is in contact with bladder and urethra
74. Posterior fornix is directly related to the recto-uterine pouch
75. Portion of levator ani forms a sling around its upper part
76. The vestibular glands (of Bartholin) open, each by a single duct, into its orifice

The anal canal:
77. Differs structurally in male and female
78. Is separated from the prostate by peritoneum
79. Is highly sensitive in its lower half
80. Lymph drains to superficial inguinal nodes
81. Is surrounded by a voluntary sphincter

The pudendal nerve:
82. Arises from 2nd, 3rd and 4th sacral nerves
83. Crosses the sacrospinous ligament
84. Passes through the centre of the ischiorectal fossa
85. Gives origin to the inferior rectal nerve
86. Is sensory to the labia majora

The ductus (vas) deferens:
87. Commences in the head of the epididymis
88. Is a constituent of the spermatic cord
89. Can be palpated on clinical examination
90. Is a boundary of the inguinal triangle
91. Terminates in the membranous urethra

Section of male pelvis

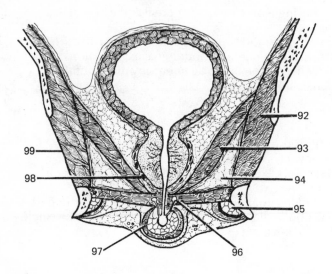

Identify the numbered structures, from the choices given below:

A   Obturator membrane
B   Prostatic venous plexus
C   Crus of penis
D   Membranous urethra
E   Retropubic space

F   Bulbospongiosus
G   Bulbourethral gland
H   Obturator internus
J   Levator ani
K   Ischiorectal fossa,
    anterior recess

Anal canal

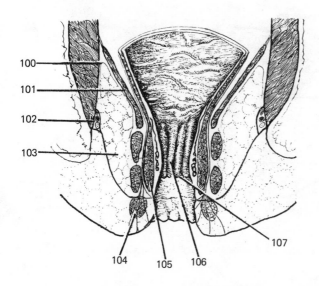

Identify the numbered structures, from the choices given below:

A   Pectinate line
B   Anal column
C   Internal anal sphincter
D   External anal sphincter
E   Pudendal canal
F   Ischiorectal fossa
G   Lunate fascia
H   Levator ani

Rectal examination

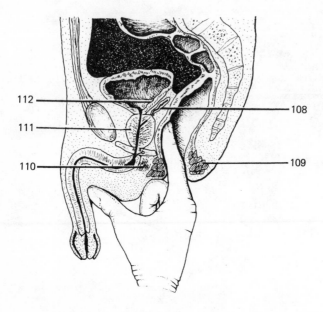

Identify the numbered structures, from the choices given below:

A Perineal body
B Perineal membrane
C Prostate
D Bulbourethral gland

E Trigone
F Rectovesical pouch
G Seminal vesicle
H Sphincter ani externus

Answers

1.	E	40.	A	77.	F
2.	C			78.	F
3.	C	41.	A	79.	T
4.	E	42.	C	80.	T
5.	E	43.	D	81.	T
6.	D	44.	C	82.	T
7.	B	45.	B	83.	T
8.	D	46.	E	84.	F
9.	A			85.	T
10.	C	47.	B	86.	T
11.	B	48.	A	87.	F
12.	E	49.	C	88.	T
13.	E	50.	A	89.	T
14.	E	51.	B	90.	F
15.	E	52.	A	91.	F
		53.	B		
16.	C	54.	C	92.	H
17.	C	55.	D	93.	J
18.	A	56.	E	94.	K
19.	B			95.	C
20.	A	57.	F	96.	G
21.	C	58.	T	97.	F
22.	C	59.	F	98.	B
23.	C	60.	T	99.	A
24.	A	61.	T		
25.	C	62.	T		
26.	C	63.	F	100.	G
27.	A	64.	F	101.	H
28.	A	65.	T	102.	E
29.	D	66.	F	103.	F
30.	C	67.	T	104.	D
31.	D	68.	T	105.	C
32.	B	69.	F	106.	B
33.	C	70.	F	107.	A
34.	A	71.	F		
35.	A	72.	F	108.	G
36.	B	73.	T	109.	H
37.	A	74.	T	110.	A
38.	A	75.	T	111.	C
39.	B	76.	T	112.	E

VI HEAD AND NECK

Questions 1–55

For each of the following multiple choice questions select the *one* most appropriate answer:

1. **Directly behind isthmus of thyroid gland:**
    A   Sternohyoid muscle
    B   Thyrohyoid muscle
    C   Oesophagus
    D   Inferior thyroid artery
    E   Trachea

2. **The common carotid artery ends at the level of the:**
    A   Sternoclavicular joint
    B   Upper border of cricoid cartilage
    C   Upper border of thyroid cartilage
    D   Lower border of mandible
    E   Neck of mandible

3. **The following structures occupy the carotid sheath, *except*:**
    A   Common carotid artery
    B   Internal carotid artery
    C   Vagus nerve
    D   Sympathetic trunk
    E   Internal jugular vein

4. **Principal adductor of vocal folds:**
    A   Lateral cricoarytenoid
    B   Posterior cricoarytenoid
    C   Aryepiglottic muscle
    D   Cricothyroid
    E   None of the above

5. **Section of the inferior (recurrent) laryngeal nerve would paralyse the intrinsic laryngeal muscles, *except:***
    A   Cricothyroid
    B   Posterior cricoarytenoid
    C   Vocalis
    D   Lateral cricoarytenoid
    E   Interarytenoid

6. **The thyroid gland is enveloped in:**
    A   Investing fascia of the neck
    B   Prevertebral fascia
    C   Pretracheal fascia
    D   Superficial fascia
    E   None of the above

7. **The cricoid cartilage is at the vertebral level of:**
    A   C2
    B   C4
    C   C6
    D   T1
    E   T3

8. **Anterior relation(s) of scalenus anterior:**
    A   Subclavian vein
    B   Phrenic nerve
    C   Brachial plexus
    D   Subclavian artery
    E   Two of the above

9. The intermediate tendon of the omohyoid muscle is anchored by a fascial sling to the:
   A Hyoid bone
   B Thyroid cartilage
   C Clavicle
   D Sternum
   E Scapula

10. The cervical plexus is formed by the ventral rami of:
    A C1, C2, C3
    B C1, C2
    C C1, C2, C3, C4
    D C3, C4
    E C3, C4, C5

11. The roots of the brachial plexus pass between:
    A Scalenus anterior and sternomastoid
    B Scalenus anterior and clavicle
    C Scalenus posterior and scalenus medius
    D Scalenus medius and scalenus posterior
    E Scalenus posterior and levator scapulae

12. Muscle attached to the first rib between subclavian vein and artery:
    A Subclavius
    B Scalenus medius
    C Scalenus anterior
    D Scalenus posterior
    E Sternomastoid

13. The larger blood vessels of the scalp run in the:
    A Skin
    B Subcutaneous tissue
    C Epicranial aponeurosis
    D Subaponeurotic tissue
    E Pericranium

14. **The plane of movement of the scalp is between:**
   A Skin and epicranial aponeurosis
   B Epicranial aponeurosis (galea aponeurotica) and pericranium
   C Skin and subcutaneous fat
   D Pericranium and skull
   E None of the above

15. **The main sensory nerve to the back of the head:**
   A Greater auricular
   B Greater occipital
   C Posterior auricular
   D Lesser occipital
   E Third occipital

16. **The zygomatic arch gives origin to:**
   A Masseter
   B Temporalis
   C Buccinator
   D Platysma
   E Medial pterygoid

17. **The main sensory nerve to the upper lip is the:**
   A Facial
   B Infraorbital
   C Buccal of mandibular
   D External nasal
   E Anterior superior alveolar

18. **The main sensory nerve to the lower lip is the:**
   A Buccal
   B Cervical of facial
   C Mental
   D Submandibular
   E Inferior labial

19. **The most horizontal fibres of temporalis muscle are:**
    A   Deep
    B   Superficial
    C   Posterior
    D   Middle
    E   Anterior

20. **A muscle which elevates and retracts the mandible:**
    A   Masseter
    B   Temporalis
    C   Medial pterygoid
    D   Lateral pterygoid
    E   Digastric

21. **A muscle attached to the coronoid process of mandible:**
    A   Buccinator
    B   Lateral pterygoid
    C   Medial pterygoid
    D   Temporalis
    E   Masseter

22. **Nerve from which the parasympathetic fibres for the parotid gland take origin:**
    A   Vagus
    B   Facial
    C   Glossopharyngeal
    D   Trigeminal
    E   Accessory

23. **The buccal branch of the mandibular nerve supplies:**
    A   Buccinator muscle
    B   Skin and mucous membrane of cheek
    C   Only skin of cheek
    D   Only mucous membrane of cheek
    E   Molar tooth pulps

24. **The following muscle assists the tongue in keeping food between the upper and lower molar teeth during mastication:**
    A   Masseter
    B   Temporalis
    C   Orbicularis oris
    D   Buccinator
    E   Risorius

25. **A structure passing deep to the hyoglossus muscle:**
    A   Hypoglossal nerve
    B   Mylohyloid nerve
    C   Submandibular duct
    D   Lingual nerve
    E   None of the above

26. **The parotid duct opens into the oral cavity opposite the crown of the:**
    A   Upper first premolar tooth
    B   Upper second molar
    C   Lower first premolar
    D   Upper third molar
    E   Lower second molar

27. **The sublingual papilla:**
    A   Is a swelling on the lingual nerve
    B   Is caused by the loop of the lingual artery
    C   Is a swelling caused by the sublingual gland
    D   Marks the opening of the submandibular duct
    E   Is a specialized taste bud

28. **The permanent dentition in each quadrant of the mouth comprises:**
    A   Two incisors, canine, two premolars, two molars
    B   One incisor, canine, two premolars, three molars
    C   Two incisors, canine, two premolars, three molars
    D   One incisor, canine, three premolars, three molars
    E   Two incisors, canine, one premolar, three molars

29. **The deciduous dentition in each quadrant of the mouth comprises:**
   A   Two incisors, canine, two molars
   B   One incisor, canine, three molars
   C   One incisor, canine, one premolar, two molars
   D   Two incisors, canine, two premolars, two molars
   E   Two incisors, canine, three molars

30. **The first permanent tooth to erupt is the:**
   A   Lateral incisor
   B   Canine
   C   First premolar
   D   First molar
   E   Third molar

31. **The first deciduous tooth to erupt is usually the:**
   A   Central incisor
   B   Canine
   C   First premolar
   D   First molar
   E   Third molar

32. **The lingual tonsil is confined to the:**
   A   Posterior one-third of the tongue
   B   Anterior one-third of the tongue
   C   Sulcus terminalis
   D   Ventral surface of the tongue
   E   None of the above

33. **The bony part of the nasal septum contains:**
   A   Perpendicular plate of ethmoid and vomer
   B   Perpendicular plate of palatine and vomer
   C   Perpendicular plate of palatine, vomer, and
        perpendicular plate of ethmoid
   D   Perpendicular plate of palatine, vomer, palatine
        crest of maxilla
   E   Perpendicular plate of vomer, palatine, rostrum of
        sphenoid

34. **Opening into the inferior meatus of the nose:**
   A   The frontal air sinus
   (B) The nasolacrimal duct
   C   The maxillary air sinus
   D   The sphenoidal air sinus
   E   Two of the above

35. **The adult maxillary air sinus always lies directly above the following teeth:**
   A   Incisors
   B   Incisors and canine
   C   Premolars
   D   Molars
   E   All of the above

36. **A branch of the maxillary nerve:**
   A   Infraorbital
   B   Supraorbital
   C   Aurticulotemporal
   D   External nasal
   E   Frontal

37. **The inferior nasal concha belongs to the:**
   A   Ethmoid
   B   Sphenoid
   C   Vomer
   D   Maxilla
   E   None of the above

38. **The geniculate ganglion is concerned with:**
   A   Secretomotor nerves to the lacrimal gland
   B   Secretomotor nerves to the submandibular gland
   C   Sensory nerves to the face
   D   Sensory nerves to the oropharynx
   E   Taste

39. **The glossopharyngeal nerve supplies the mucous membrane of:**
   A   Nasopharynx
   B   Oropharynx
   C   Laryngopharynx
   D   Larynx
   E   All of the above

40. **The following dural venous sinus occupies the tentorium cerebelli:**
   A   Sphenoparietal
   B   Inferior petrosal
   C   Straight
   D   Inferior sagittal
   E   Occipital

41. **Structure directly anterior to the jugular foramen:**
   A   Styloid process
   B   Occipital condyle
   C   Foramen magnum
   D   Sphenoidal spine
   E   Carotid canal

42. **The following bony parts ossify from membranous precursors, *except:***
   A   Lesser wings of sphenoid
   B   Pterygoid plates of sphenoid
   C   Squamous temporal
   D   Petrous temporal
   E   Tympanic plate

43. **Directly lateral to the jugular foramen:**
   A   Carotid canal
   B   Styloid process
   C   Mastoid process
   D   Lateral pterygoid plate
   E   Hypoglossal canal

44. **Embedded in the parotid gland:**
   A   Facial nerve
   B   External carotid artery
   C   Retromandibular vein
   D   Lymph nodes
   E   All the above

45. **The following belong to the sphenoid bone, *except:***
   A   Crista galli
   B   Anterior clinoid process
   C   Lateral pterygoid plate
   D   Sella turcica
   E   Optic foramen

46. **The hypoglossal nerve supplies the following muscles, *except:***
   A   Hypoglossus
   B   Inferior longitudinal muscle of the tongue
   C   Genioglossus
   D   Styloglossus
   E   Mylohyoid

47. **Origin from internal carotid artery:**
   A   Lingual
   B   Facial
   C   Superior thyroid
   D   Inferior thyroid
   E   None of the above

48. **The main artery to the palatine tonsil comes from the:**
   A   Lingual
   B   Faucial
   C   Facial
   D   Submandibular
   E   Sublingual

49. **Transmitted by the carotid canal:**
    A   External carotid artery
    B   Sympathetic nerves to the eye
    C   The facial nerve
    D   The vagus nerve
    E   None of the above

50. **Commonly found in abducent nerve paralysis:**
    A   Ptosis
    B   Convergent squint
    C   Loss of upward gaze
    D   Loss of medial gaze
    E   Loss of accommodation

51. **In contact with the tympanic membrane:**
    A   Chorda tympani nerve
    B   Facial nerve
    C   Incus
    D   Tensor tympani
    E   Stapes

52. **The superior orbital fissure is bounded by the:**
    A   Maxilla and greater wing of sphenoid
    B   Maxilla and lesser wing of sphenoid
    C   Lesser wing of sphenoid and ethmoidal
    D   Lesser wing and greater wing of sphenoid
    E   Lesser wing of sphenoid and frontal

53. **Bone(s) forming the lateral margin of the orbit:**
    A   Zygomatic
    B   Frontal
    C   Zygomatic and frontal
    D   Zygomatic and sphenoidal
    E   Frontal and sphenoidal

54. **Opening of the middle ear in which the footplate of the stapes is placed:**
    A   Opening of pyramid
    B   Oval window (fenestra vestibuli)
    C   Aditus
    D   Tubal opening
    E   Round window (fenestra cochleae)

55. **The main sensory nerve to the pinna of the ear:**
    A   Great auricular
    B   Greater occipital
    C   Zygomatico-facial
    D   Zygomatico-temporal
    E   Lesser occipital

Questions 56–95

The set of lettered headings below is followed by a list of numbered words or phrases. For each numbered word or phrase select the correct answer under:

A   If the item is associated with A only
B   If the item is associated with B only
C   If the item is associated with both A and B
D   If the item is associated with neither A nor B

    A   Lateral pterygoid
    B   Medial pterygoid
    C   Both
    D   Neither

56. Attached to articular disc of temporomandibular joint
57. Attached to neck of mandible
58. Assists in opening the mouth
59. Assists in closing the mouth

A   Facial nerve
B   Mandibular nerve
C   Both
D   Neither

60. Motor to buccinator
61. Motor to medial pterygoid
62. Sensory to upper lip
63. Sensory to lower lip

A   Foramen ovale
B   Foramen spinosum
C   Both
D   Neither

64. Maxillary nerve
65. Mandibular nerve
66. Facial nerve
67. Branches of maxillary artery

A   Hyoglossus
B   Genioglossus
C   Both
D   Neither

68. Hypoglossal nerve supply
69. Contact with submandibular gland
70. Superficial to lingual artery
71. Attached to mandible

A   Middle meatus of nose
B   Inferior meatus of nose
C   Both
D   Neither

72. Orifice of frontal air sinus
73. Orifice of nasolacrimal duct
74. Orifice of sphenoidal air sinus
75. Lined by olfactory epithelium
76. Origin from stomodaeum of embryo

A   Superior petrosal sinus
B   Sigmoid sinus
C   Both
D   Neither

77.   Is an air sinus
78.   Direct communication with cavernous sinus
79.   Groove(s) the temporal bone
80.   Posterior relation of tympanic cavity

A   Superior rectus muscle of eye
B   Inferior oblique muscle of eye
C   Both
D   Neither

81.   Oculomotor nerve supply
82.   Looking upwards
83.   Looking downwards
84.   Looking downwards and outwards
85.   Muscle spindles are present

A   Ophthalmic nerve
B   Facial nerve
C   Both
D   Neither

86.   Light reflex
87.   Accommodation reflex
88.   Corneal reflex
89.   Consensual reflex
90.   Jaw jerk

A   Tympanic cavity
B   Epitympanic recess
C   Both
D   Neither

91.   Related to facial nerve
92.   Leads directly into mastoid antrum
93.   Leads directly into Eustachian tube
94.   Related directly to tympanic membrane
95.   Derived from ectoderm of first pharyngeal groove (cleft)

Questions 96–110

Directions: In the following series of questions, one or more of the four items is/are correct.

Answer A   if 1, 2 and 3 are correct
        B   if 1 and 3 are correct
        C   if 2 and 4 are correct
        D   if only 4 is correct
and   E   if all four are correct

96. **The contracting sternomastoid:**
    1. Rotates the head to the opposite side
    2. Tilts the head to the same side
    3. Flexes the neck
    4. May assist inspiration

97. **Active in opening the mouth:**
    1. Medial pterygoid
    2. Digastric
    3. Masseter
    4. Lateral pterygoid

98. **Haemostats placed on the inferior thyroid artery may endanger:**
    1. The inferior (recurrent) laryngeal nerve
    2. The external laryngeal nerve
    3. The cervical sympathetic chain
    4. The phrenic nerve

99. **The vocal folds are abducted by:**
    1. Thyro-arytenoids
    2. Lateral crico-arytenoids
    3. Inter-arytenoids
    4. Posterior crico-arytenoids

100. **Origin of buccinator muscle:**
    1. Pterygomandibular raphe
    2. Maxilla above molar teeth
    3. Mandible below molar teeth
    4. Coronoid process

101. **The vocal folds are attached to the:**
    1. Hyoid bone
    2. Thyroid cartilage
    3. Cricoid cartilage
    4. Arytenoid cartilages

102. **The cricopharyngeus muscle is:**
    1. Part of the middle constrictor of the pharynx
    2. Innervated by inferior (recurrent) laryngeal nerve
    3. Composed of smooth muscle fibres
    4. Horizontally disposed

103. **The sensory supply of the pulps of the upper teeth is by:**
    1. Posterior superior alveolar nerve
    2. Middle superior alveolar nerve
    3. Anterior superior alveolar nerve
    4. Infraorbital nerve

104. **The soft palate:**
    1. Separates nasopharynx from oropharynx
    2. Is elevated mainly by tensor palati
    3. May be occupied by portion of the tonsil
    4. Contains the horizontal plate of the palatine bone

105. **Ocular sign(s) of sympathetic paralysis:**
    1. Constricted pupil
    2. Raised eyelid
    3. Ptosis
    4. Exophthalmos

106. **The straight sinus:**
    1. Occupies the line of attachment of falx cerebri to vault of skull
    2. Is formed by union of the great cerebral vein and inferior sagittal sinus
    3. Is commonly absent
    4. Enters the confluence of sinuses

107. **The upper eyelid:**
   1. Contains modified sebaceous glands
   2. Is strengthened by the tarsus
   3. Is raised by contraction of levator palpebrae superioris
   4. Is lowered by contraction of orbicularis oculi

108. **The lacrimal sac:**
   1. Lies against the upper lateral wall of the orbit
   2. Is emptied by blinking
   3. Secretes the tears
   4. Opens into the nasolacrimal duct

109. **Accommodation of the eye is associated with contraction of the:**
   1. Dilator pupillae
   2. Sphincter pupillae
   3. Orbicularis oculi
   4. Ciliary muscle

110. **The abducent nerve innervates the:**
   1. Superior rectus
   2. Medial rectus
   3. Inferior rectus
   4. Lateral rectus

Questions 111–128

The group of questions below consists of numbered headings, followed by a list of lettered words or phrases. For each heading select the *one* word or phrase which is most closely related to it. *Note:* Each choice may be used *once only.*

111.	Submental lymph nodes	A	Tip of tongue
112.	Submandibular lymph nodes	B	Lower molar teeth
		C	Outer canthus of eye
113.	Preauricular lymph nodes		
114.	Mastoid lymph nodes	D	Posterior third of tongue
		E	None of the above

115.	Internal carotid artery	A	Pterygomaxillary
116.	External carotid artery		fissure
117.	Vertebral artery	B	Foramen magnum
118.	Maxillary artery	C	Carotid foramen
119.	Middle meningeal	D	Foramen spinosum
	artery	E	None of the above

120.	Maxillary nerve	A	Foramen ovale
121.	Nervus spinosus	B	Foramen spinosum
122.	Mandibular nerve	C	Stylomastoid foramen
123.	Facial nerve	D	Jugular foramen
124.	Glossopharyngeal	E	Foramen rotundum
	nerve		

125.	Temporalis	A	Opening the mouth
126.	Mylohyoid	B	Closing the mouth
127.	Orbicularis oculi	C	Opening the eye
128.	Levator palpebrae	D	Closing the eye
	superioris		

Questions 129–203

In reply to the following questions indicate whether you think each statement is *True* or *False*:

In the neck:
129. The recurrent laryngeal nerve supplies cricothyroid
130. The recurrent laryngeal nerve branches contact those of the superior thyroid artery
131. The inferior thyroid artery passes behind the carotid sheath
132. The sympathetic chain occupies the carotid sheath
133. The phrenic nerve descends on the anterior surface of scalenus anterior

The external jugular vein:
134. Is formed by the junction of the superficial temporal and maxillary veins
135. Crosses the sternomastoid to enter the posterior triangle
136. Because it lies beneath the deep fascia, is never visible in the living
137. Usually terminates in the subclavian vein
138. Because it lacks competent valves, it is an important indicator of pressure changes in the right atrium

The posterior triangle of the neck:
139. Is bordered by sternomastoid, mandible and trapezius
140. Has the eleventh cranial nerve in its floor
141. Is confined to the posterior aspect of the neck
142. Contains the trunks of the brachial plexus
143. Contains numerous lymph nodes

The spinal accessory nerve:
144. Arises entirely from the spinal cord
145. Enters the skull via the foramen magnum
146. Leaves the skull via the jugular foramen
147. Contributes to the pharyngeal plexus of nerves
148. Injury in the posterior triangle results in wasting of the trapezius on the same side

The thyroid gland:
149. Is closely related to inferior (recurrent) laryngeal nerve
150. Moves on swallowing
151. Isthmus is at level of thyroid cartilage
152. Is invested by pretracheal fascia together with the parathyroids
153. Accessory thyroid tissue is sometimes present close to internal jugular vein

The ophthalmic nerve:
154. Enters the orbit through the optic foramen
155. Carries corneal sensation
156. Is motor to levator palpebrae superioris
157. Is sensory to the upper teeth
158. When injured the light reflex is abolished on the same side

The maxillary nerve:
159. Arises from the trigeminal ganglion
160. Occupies the lateral wall of the cavernous sinus
161. Has the otic ganglion attached to it
162. Supplies the skin of the bridge of the nose
163. Is entirely sensory

The facial nerve:
164. Leaves the skull through foramen spinosum
165. Supplies sensory fibres to the conjunctiva
166. Is motor to the buccinator
167. Carries secreto-motor fibres for the parotid gland
168. Provides one limb of the corneal reflex arc

The hypoglossal nerve:
169. Supplies sensation to the anterior part of the tongue
170. Carries fibres from the second and third cervical nerves
171. Passes between the internal and external carotid arteries
172. Is motor to both intrinsic and extrinsic muscles of the tongue
173. Following paralysis, the tongue on protrusion deviates towards the affected side

In the temporo-mandibular joint:
174. Contact is between mandible and tympanic plate
175. Articular surface includes the eminentia articularis
176. Gliding movements take place in the upper compartment
177. Rotatory movement takes place in the lower compartment
178. Axis of joint rotation passes through the head of the mandible

The parotid gland:
179. Is wedged between trapezius and mandible
180. Is covered by investing layer of cervical fascia
181. Contains the facial artery
182. Has lymph nodes buried in its substance
183. Its duct pierces buccinator to enter the mouth

The submandibular salivary gland:
184. Has two lobes
185. Discharges into the mouth via the sublingual papilla
186. Lies entirely deep to the mylohyoid
187. Receives secreto-motor fibres from the submandibular ganglion
188. Has only one duct

The sublingual gland:
189. Occupies the sublingual fold in floor of mouth
190. Lies between mylohyoid and digastric muscles
191. Has only one large duct
192. Secreto-motor nerves travel via chorda tympani and lingual nerves
193. Lies on the submandibular duct

The lingual nerve:
194. Leaves the skull through the pterygomaxillary fissure
195. Carries fibres from the first cervical spinal nerve
196. Is closely related to the mandible behind the third molar tooth
197. Carries secreto-motor fibres to the submandibular salivary gland
198. Carries fibres for both taste and common sensation from the anterior tongue

The middle meningeal artery:
199. Is a branch of the internal carotid
200. Enters the skull through the foramen spinosum
201. Gives a branch to the circle of Willis
202. Divides in the region of the pterion
203. Haemorrhage from the artery is usually subdural

Base of Skull

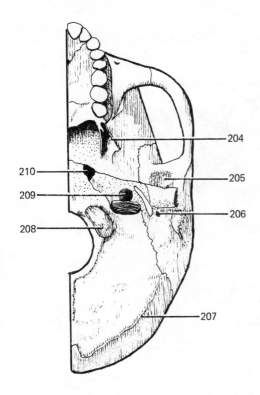

Identify the numbered structures, from the choices given below:

A   Lateral pterygoid plate   E   Foramen lacerum
B   Carotid canal   F   Articular fossa
C   Occipital condyle   G   Inferior nuchal line
D   Stylomastoid foramen   H   Superior nuchal line

Intratemporal fossa

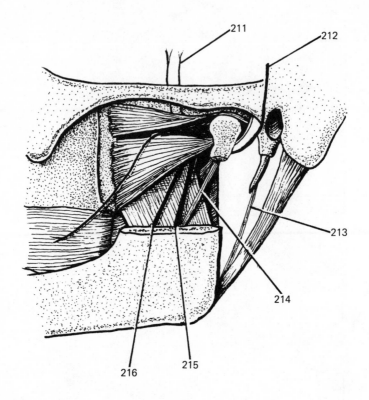

Identify the numbered structures, from the choices given below:

A   Lingual nerve
B   Inferior alveolar nerve
C   Deep temporal nerve
D   Buccal branch of
    mandibular nerve

E   Stylomandibular
    ligament
F   Sphenomandibular
    ligament
G   Medial pterygoid
H   Auriculotemporal
    nerve

Deep structures of neck

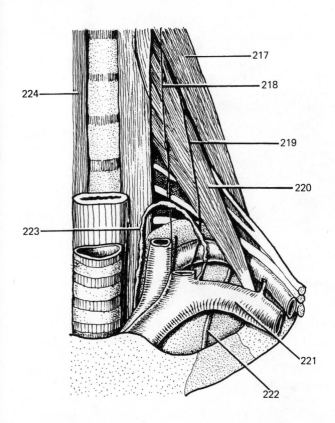

217
218
224
219
220
223
221
222

Identify the numbered structures, from the choices given below:

A	Scalenus anterior	F	Brachial plexus
B	Scalenus medius	G	Sympathetic trunk
C	Longus colli	H	Subclavian vein
D	Internal thoracic artery	J	Phrenic nerve
E	Thoracic duct	K	Vagus nerve

Section of neck

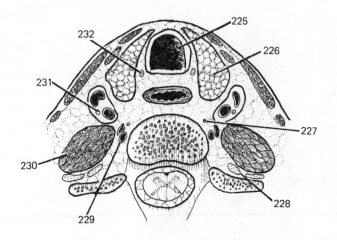

Identify the numbered structures, from the choices given below:

A	Scalenus anterior	F	Vagus nerve
B	Trachea	G	Oesophagus
C	Scalenus medius	H	Vertebral artery
D	Thyroid gland	J	Brachial plexus
E	Sympathetic trunk	K	Recurrent laryngeal nerve

Larynx

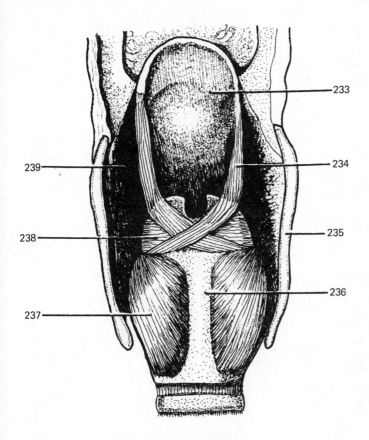

Identify the numbered structures, from the choices given below:

A	Interarytenoid	E	Posterior cricoarytenoid
B	Cricoid cartilage	F	Epiglottis
C	Thyroid cartilage	G	Aryepiglotticus
D	Vallecula	H	Pyriform fossa

Answers

1.	E	43.	B	84.	D
2.	C	44.	E	85.	C
3.	D	45.	A	86.	D
4.	A	46.	E	87.	D
5.	A	47.	E	88.	C
6.	C	48.	C	89.	D
7.	C	49.	B	90.	D
8.	E	50.	B	91.	C
9.	C	51.	A	92.	B
10.	C	52.	D	93.	A
11.	C	53.	C	94.	A
12.	C	54.	B	95.	D
13.	B	55.	A		
14.	B				
15.	B	56.	A	96.	E
16.	A	57.	A	97.	C
17.	B	58.	A	98.	B
18.	C	59.	B	99.	D
19.	C	60.	A	100.	A
20.	B	61.	B	101.	C
21.	D	62.	D	102.	C
22.	C	63.	B	103.	A
23.	B	64.	D	104.	B
24.	D	65.	A	105.	B
25.	E	66.	D	106.	C
26.	B	67.	C	107.	E
27.	D	68.	C	108.	C
28.	C	69.	A	109.	C
29.	A	70.	A	110.	D
30.	D	71.	B		
31.	A	72.	A	111.	A
32.	A	73.	B	112.	B
33.	A	74.	D	113.	C
34.	B	75.	D	114.	E
35.	D	76.	C	115.	C
36.	A	77.	D	116.	E
37.	E	78.	A	117.	B
38.	E	79.	C	118.	A
39.	B	80.	B	119.	D
40.	C	81.	C	120.	E
41.	E	82.	C	121.	B
42.	D	83.	D	122.	A

123. C	163. T	204. A
124. D	164. F	205. F
125. B	165. F	206. D
126. A	166. T	207. H
127. D	167. F	208. C
128. C	168. T	209. B
	169. F	210. E
129. F	170. T	
130. F	171. F	211. C
131. T	172. T	212. H
132. F	173. T	213. E
133. T	174. F	214. F
134. F	175. T	215. B
135. T	176. T	216. A
136. F	177. T	
137. T	178. F	217. B
138. T	179. F	218. G
139. F	180. T	219. J
140. T	181. F	220. A
141. F	182. T	221. H
142. T	183. T	222. D
143. T	184. T	223. E
144. T	185. T	224. C
145. T	186. F	
146. T	187. T	225. B
147. F	188. T	226. D
148. T	189. T	227. E
149. T	190. F	228. J
150. T	191. F	229. H
151. F	192. T	230. A
152. T	193. T	231. F
153. T	194. F	232. K
154. F	195. F	
155. T	196. T	233. F
156. F	197. T	234. G
157. F	198. T	235. C
158. F	199. F	236. B
159. T	200. T	237. E
160. T	201. F	238. A
161. F	202. T	239. H
162. F	203. F	

VII NERVOUS SYSTEM

Questions 1–50

For each of the following multiple choice questions select the *one* most appropriate answer:

1. **In the 'motor nerve' entering a muscle, sensory fibres make up the following proportion:**
    A   None
    B   20 per cent
    C   40 per cent
    D   75 per cent
    E   90 per cent

2. **Pacinian corpuscles are numerous in:**
    A   The dermis of the skin
    B   Periarticular tissues
    C   Bone marrow
    D   Muscle
    E   Intestine

3. **The rate of regeneration of peripheral nerves following injury is:**
    A   1–3 micra per day
    B   1–3 mm per hour
    C   1–3 mm per day
    D   1–3 mm per week
    E   1–3 mm per month

4. **In the postnatal period the greatest growth in the grey matter of the CNS is of:**
   A   Nerve cell numbers
   B   Length of axonal processes
   C   Dendritic trees
   D   Size of perikarya
   E   None of the above

5. **The cells of the posterior grey horn of the spinal cord are arranged:**
   A   In clusters
   B   In laminae from apex to base
   C   In laminae from medial to lateral side
   D   Diffusely
   E   In alternating large and small cell groups

6. **Grossly the spinal cord presents two swellings:**
   A   Cervical and thoracic
   B   Cervical and lumbar
   C   Thoracic and lumbar
   D   Thoracic and sacral
   E   Lumbar and sacral

7. **The internal vertebral venous plexus occupies:**
   A   The extradural space
   B   The subdural space
   C   The subarachnoid space
   D   The spinal cord
   E   The foramen transversarium

8. **The internal vertebral venous plexus communicates with:**
   A   Vertebral bone marrow
   B   Segmental veins
   C   Intracranial sinuses
   D   Pelvic venous plexuses
   E   All the above

9. **Inferior cerebral veins terminate in the:**
   A   Transverse sinus
   B   Cavernous sinus
   C   Sigmoid sinus
   D   Great cerebral vein
   E   Inferior sagittal sinus

10. **The subarachnoid space reaches to vertebral level:**
    A   T12 or L1
    B   L1 or L2
    C   L4 or L5
    D   S2
    E   Tip of coccyx

11. **A disc prolapse at L5 level, in the usual position of extrusion, may compress:**
    A   L3, 4 and 5 nerve roots
    B   L4 roots
    C   L5 roots
    D   S1 roots
    E   All the above

12. **In eliciting a tendon reflex, the sequence of neurones activated is:**
    A   Tendon afferent, internuncial, alpha efferent
    B   Spindle afferent, internuncial, alpha efferent
    C   Spindle afferent, internuncial, gamma efferent
    D   Tendon afferent, alpha efferent
    E   Spindle afferent, alpha efferent

13. **Commonest level of termination of the adult spinal cord:**
    A   T12–L1 disc
    B   L1–L2 disc
    C   L3–L4 disc
    D   L5–S1 disc
    E   Second sacral vertebra

14. **The cell in the CNS most like the Schwann cell in function is the:**
   A   Fibrous astrocyte
   B   Protoplasmic astrocyte
   C   Microglial cell
   D   Pericyte
   E   Oligodendrocyte

15. **In the CNS, portions of first order sensory neurones are found:**
   A   In the posterior columns
   B   In the posterolateral tract of Lissauer
   C   In the lateral columns
   D   In the anterior columns
   E   Two of the above

16. **The sacral segments of the spinal cord may be crushed by fracture of:**
   A   The first lumbar vertebra
   B   The third lumbar vertebra
   C   The fifth lumbar vertebra
   D   The first and second sacral vertebrae
   E   None of the above

17. **Axons from the nucleus ambiguus innervate muscles of the:**
   A   Eye
   B   Tongue
   C   Larynx
   D   Ear
   E   Jaws

18. **A classical sign of cerebellar disease:**
   A   Rigidity
   B   Short, shuffling gait
   C   Loss of 'joint sense'
   D   Spasticity
   E   Intention tremor

19. **Tract which is small or absent in humans:**
   A   Rubrospinal
   B   Tectospinal
   C   Vestibulospinal
   D   Olivospinal
   E   Anterior corticospinal

20. **A midline nucleus in the medulla oblongata:**
   A   Hypoglossal nucleus
   B   Nucleus ambiguus
   C   Dorsal vagal nucleus
   D   Nucleus raphe magnus
   E   Central reticular nucleus

21. **The cerebellum sends efferent fibres to each of the following, *except*:**
   A   The red nucleus of the opposite side
   B   The thalamus of the opposite side
   C   Reticular formation
   D   The vestibular nuclei of the same side
   E   The substantia nigra

22. **The structure closest to the crus cerebri is the:**
   A   Substantia nigra
   B   Red nucleus
   C   Medial lemniscus
   D   Opposite crus
   E   Superior cerebellar peduncle

23. **The cerebral aqueduct (of Sylvius) connects:**
   A   The lateral ventricles
   B   Lateral and third ventricles
   C   Third and fourth ventricles
   D   Fourth ventricle and subarachnoid space
   E   Fourth ventricle and central canal of spinal cord

24. **The following structure occupies the floor of the temporal horn of the lateral ventricle:**
   A Stria vascularis
   B Calcar avis
   C Diagonal band of Broca
   D Amygdala
   E Hippocampus

25. **The interventricular foramen of Monro connects:**
   A The two lateral ventricles
   B Lateral ventricle with third ventricle
   C Third and fourth ventricles
   D Fourth ventricle with subarachnoid space
   E Tela choroidea with third ventricle

26. **Betz cells constitute the following percentage of the corticospinal tract neurones:**
   A 0
   B 3
   C 10
   D 50
   E 100

27. **The crus cerebri contains:**
   A Medial lemniscus
   B Spinothalamic tract
   C Temporopontine fibres
   D Lateral lemniscus
   E None of the above

28. **Folds of the cerebral cortex overlying the insula are called the:**
   A Temporal lobes
   B Corpus callosum
   C Opercula
   D Commissures of the fornix
   E Pallia

29. **Nystagmus depends upon connections between vestibular and oculomotor nuclei via:**
    A   Medial longitudinal bundle
    B   Medial lemniscus
    C   Reticular formation
    D   Spinal lemniscus
    E   Central grey matter

30. **The retrolentiform (retrolenticular) part of the internal capsule contains:**
    A   The optic radiation
    B   The pyramidal tract
    C   The main thalamocortical system
    D   Frontopontine fibres
    E   Temporopontine fibres

31. **Broca's area occupies the:**
    A   Superior frontal gyrus
    B   Middle frontal gyrus
    C   Inferior frontal gyrus
    D   Superior temporal gyrus
    E   Inferior temporal gyrus

32. **The cells of origin of the optic radiation occupy the:**
    A   Ganglion cell layer of retina
    B   Medial geniculate nucleus
    C   Lateral geniculate nucleus
    D   Superior colliculus
    E   Occipital cortex

33. **Buried in the lateral sulcus of the cerebral hemisphere is the:**
    A   Occipital lobe
    B   Splenium
    C   Operculum
    D   Insula
    E   Pars triangularis

34. Neurological examination of a patient reveals right-sided hemiparesis, increased tendon reflexes, and a Babinski sign. Which of the following is the most likely site of the lesion?
   A   Left occipital cortex
   B   Left frontal lobe
   C   Left internal capsule
   D   Optic chiasma
   E   Right thalamus

35. The above patient's symptomatology would lead you to expect, on the right side:
   A   Analgesia
   B   Absent abdominal reflexes
   C   Cerebellar signs
   D   Abnormal pupillary reactions
   E   Fasciculation of muscles

36. A cranial nerve lesion corresponding to an upper motor neurone lesion of a spinal nerve is called:
   A   Suprasegmental
   B   Supratentorial
   C   Supranuclear
   D   Supramarginal
   E   Supraorbital

37. The ganglionic cells of the retina are homologous with:
   A   Posterior root ganglion neurones
   B   Posterior grey horn neurones
   C   Anterior grey horn neurones
   D   Autonomic ganglia
   E   None of the above

38. The following structures are found at the level of the nucleus of the oculomotor nerve, *except:*
   A   Red nucleus
   B   Pretectal nucleus
   C   Substantia nigra
   D   Decussation of the superior cerebellar peduncles
   E   Superior collicus

39. **The abducent nerve is especially liable to be compressed by a rise in intracranial pressure because:**
    A   It emerges at the lower border of the pons
    B   It is related to the basisphenoid
    C   It crosses the sharp apex of the petrous temporal bone
    D   It traverses the superior orbital fissure
    E   It traverses the subarachnoid space

40. **Fibres from the dorsal cochlear nucleus join fibres from the ventral cochlear nucleus in the:**
    A   Nucleus of the vestibular nerve
    B   Trapezoid body
    C   Medial longitudinal fasciculus
    D   Medial lemniscus
    E   None of the above

41. **The nucleus ambiguus gives origin to motor fibres that run in the — nerves:**
    A   Vagus, trigeminal and facial
    B   Glossopharyngeal and vagus
    C   Vagus, hypoglossal and facial
    D   Facial, abducent and oculomotor
    E   Trigeminal, abducent and facial.

42. **In the human brain, the red nucleus projects mainly to the:**
    A   Ipsilateral cerebellar cortex
    B   Ipsilateral inferior olivary nucleus
    C   Contralateral dentate nucleus
    D   Contralateral anterior grey horn
    E   Ipsilateral thalamus

43. **Basal forebrain and brain stem are linked by fibre systems running in the:**
    A   Central tegmental tract
    B   Fornix
    C   Posterior longitudinal fasciculus
    D   Medial forebrain bundle
    E   Inferior longitudinal fasciculus

44. **Hypothalamic neurones containing large secretory granules:**
   A   Suprachiasmatic
   B   Posterior
   C   Paraventricular
   D   Posterior
   E   Ventromedial

45. **In the hypothalamus, dopaminergic neurones are concentrated in the – nucleus:**
   A   Arcuate
   B   Supraoptic
   C   Ventromedial
   D   Preoptic
   E   Paraventricular

46. **In the hypothalamus, the tuberinfundibular tract terminates in the:**
   A   Median eminence
   B   Midbrain
   C   Adenohypophysis
   D   Arcuate nucleus
   E   Limbic cortex

47. **The hypothalamohypophyseal tract terminates in the:**
   A   Median eminence
   B   Tuber cinereum
   C   Anterior lobe of pituitary gland
   D   Posterior lobe of pituitary gland
   E   All the above

48. **Spinoreticular fibres are relayed rostrally to the — nucleus of thalamus:**
   A   Intralaminar
   B   Mediodorsal
   C   Anterior
   D   Lateral posterior
   E   Ventral lateral

49   The medial lemniscus and the spinothalamic tract both
      terminate in the — nucleus of thalamus:
      A   Anterior
      B   Ventral anterior
      C   Ventral lateral
      D   Ventral posterior
      E   Lateral posterior

50.   A thalamic nucleus composed of recurrent inhibitory
      neurones:
      A   Laterodorsal
      B   Parafascicular
      C   Centromedian
      D   Reticular
      E   Pulvinar

Questions 51–76

The set of lettered headings below is followed by a list of
numbered words or phrases. For each numbered word or phrase
select the correct answer under:

      A   If the item is associated with A only
      B   If the item is associated with B only
      C   If the item is associated with both A and B
      D   If the item is associated with neither A nor B

      A   Unipolar nerve cells
      B   Multipolar nerve cells
      C   Both
      D   Neither

51.   Found in sympathetic ganglia
52.   Found in dorsal grey horn of spinal cord
53.   Restricted to sensory pathways
54.   Usually no synapse in vicinity
55.   Derived from embryonic bipolar neurones

A   Dorsal grey horn
B   Ventral grey horn
C   Both
D   Neither

56. Termination of pyramidal tract
57. Origin of fasciculus cuneatus
58. All neurones are multipolar
59. Origin of parasympathetic outflow
60. Propriospinal neurones are present
61. Renshaw cells are present

A   Alphamotoneurones
B   Gamma motoneurones
C   Both
D   Neither

62. Cell bodies occupy dorsal grey horns
63. Distributed exclusively to extrafusal muscle fibres
64. Axons terminate in motor end plates
65. Stimulated directly by primary spindle afferents
66. Are synonymous with Renshaw cells

A   Upper motor neurone lesion
B   Lower motor neurone lesion
C   Both
D   Neither

67. Characterized by rapid wasting
68. Characterized by fasciculation
69. Characterized by weakness
70. Characterized by loss of reflexes
71. Characterized by Babinski sign

A   Anterior cerebral artery
B   Middle cerebral artery
C   Both
D   Neither

72. Blood supply to 'leg area' of motor cortex
73. Blood supply to full anteroposterior length of the internal
    capsule
74. Blood supply to auditory cortex
75. Blood supply to visual cortex
76. In contact with corpus callosum

Questions 77–94

Directions: In the following series of questions, one or more of the four items is/are correct.

Answer A   if 1, 2 and 3 are correct
        B   if 1 and 3 are correct
        C   if 2 and 4 are correct
        D   if only 4 is correct
and   E   if all four are correct

77. **Organelles required for rapid axoplasmic transport mechanism:**
    1. Nissl bodies
    2. Ribosomes
    3. Synaptic vesicles
    4. Microtubules

78. **Synaptic boutons may be found on the:**
    1. Soma
    2. Axon hillock
    3. Dendrites
    4. Initial unmyelinated segment

79. **Terminal knobs (boutons terminaux) contain:**
    1. Synaptic vesicles
    2. Mitochondria
    3. Microtubules
    4. Ribosomes

80. **Synapses are present in:**
    1. Sympathetic ganglia
    2. Parasympathetic ganglia
    3. Neuromuscular junctions
    4. Spinal ganglia

81. **Annulospiral nerve endings are activated by:**
    1. Contraction of intrafusal muscle fibres
    2. Stretch of antagonist muscles
    3. Stretch of related extrafusal muscle fibres
    4. Contraction of related extrafusal muscle fibres

82. **Lower motor neurone lesions are characterized by:**
    1. Flaccidity
    2. Loss of reflexes at the same segmental level
    3. Wasting
    4. Sensory loss

83. **Upper motor neurone lesions are characterized by:**
    1. Spasticity
    2. Increased tendon reflexes
    3. Babinski sign
    4. Absent abdominal reflexes

84. **Left-sided hemisection of spinal cord in the mid-thoracic region may produce:**
    1. Loss of pain sensation in the left leg
    2. Loss of pain sensation in the right leg
    3. Loss of vibration sense in the right leg
    4. Loss of vibration sense in the left leg

85. **Part(s) of cerebellum in median plane:**
    1. Flocculus
    2. Nodule
    3. Tonsil
    4. Vermis

86. **The nucleus solitarius is concerned with:**
    1. Baroreceptor reflex
    2. Touch
    3. Taste
    4. Smell

87. **The nucleus ambiguus:**
    1. Innervates striated muscle of branchial origin
    2. Contributes to the facial nerve
    3. Occupies the lateral part of the medulla oblongata
    4. Is usually absent in man

88. **The reticular formation:**
    1. Occupies medulla, pons and midbrain
    2. Is played upon by fibres from the cerebral cortex
    3. Is influenced by the cerebellum
    4. Is concerned in reflexes regulating muscle tone

89. **The pretectal nucleus is on the pathway of the — reflex:**
    1. Light
    2. Accommodation
    3. Consensual
    4. Convergence

90. **A left homonymous hemianopia can be produced by a lesion in the right:**
    1. Occipital cortex
    2. Optical radiation
    3. Optic tract
    4. Optic nerve

91. **Visual-auditory conversion area(s):**
    1. Supramarginal gyrus
    2. Broca's area
    3. Wernicke's area
    4. Angular gyrus

92. **Component fibres of internal capsule:**
    1. Thalamocortical
    2. Corticospinal
    3. Corticobulbar
    4. Corticoreticular

93. **Synonym(s) for primary visual cortex:**
    1. Striate cortex
    2. Area 17
    3. Calcarine cortex
    4. Occipital lobe

94. **Branch(es) of the internal carotid artery:**
    1. Ophthalmic
    2. Anterior cerebral
    3. Middle cerebral
    4. Posterior cerebral

Questions 95–109

The group of questions below consists of five lettered headings, followed by a list of numbered phrases. For each numbered phrase select the *one* heading which is most closely related to it.
Note: each choice may be used *only once.*

95. Unipolar nerve cells	A	Posterior nerve roots
96. Preganglionic sympathetic nerve fibres	B	Anterior horn cells
	C	Grey rami communicantes
97. Multipolar neurones	D	Ventral rami
98. Cervical plexus	E	None of the above
99. Postganglionic sympathetic nerve fibres		

100. Between pons and middle cerebellar peduncle	A	Trigeminal nerve roots
	B	Abducent nerve
101. Between pons and pyramid	C	Facial nerve
102. Between pyramid and olive	D	Glossopharyngeal nerve
103. Between olive and inferior cerebellar peduncle	E	Hypoglossal nerve
104. Between pons and olive		

105. Arm area of motor cortex	A	Anterior cerebral artery
106. Visuosensory cortex	B	Middle cerebral artery
107. Leg area of sensory cortex	C	Posterior cerebral artery
108. Medulla oblongata	D	Basilar artery
109. Pons	E	Posterior inferior cerebellar artery

Questions 110–134

In reply to the following questions indicate whether you think each statement is *True* or *False*.

Following section of a peripheral nerve:
110. The endoneurium in the distal stump undergoes a gradual increase in thickness
111. Myelin sheaths in the distal stump break up and are phagocytosed
112. Axis cylinders break up simultaneously throughout the entire length of the distal stump
113. Schwann cells migrate from both cut surfaces to bridge the gap
114. The parent cells undergo chromatolysis

Regenerating peripheral nerves:
115. Require the support of living Schwann cells in the peripheral stump
116. Grow at the same rate in motor and sensory nerves of similar size
117. In muscle, re-establish neuromuscular junctions at the original locations
118. Enter the distal stump in large numbers provided apposition of cut ends is good
119. Acquire new myelin sheaths as they traverse the distal stump

The following ultrastructural features characterize a synapse:
120. Thickening of the apposed plasma membranes
121. The presence of clear vesicles in the axon terminal
122. The presence of dense-core vesicles in the adjacent region of dendrite or soma
123. Intrusion of delicate glial processes into the synaptic cleft
124. Tight junctions at the margins of the synaptic cleft

The substantia nigra:
125. Is restricted to the midbrain
126. Projects to ventrolateral nucleus of thalamus
127. Appears to be mainly inhibitory in function
128. Is composed of monoaminergic neurones
129. Becomes darker in Parkinson's disease

In the cerebellum:
130. Granule cells synapse only on Purkinje cell dendrites
131. The total output from the cortex is inhibitory
132. Efferents from the dentate nucleus form the bulk of the superior cerebellar peduncle
133. Blood supply is exclusively from the basilar artery
134. Disease of one hemisphere results in contralateral signs in the limbs

Horizontal section of brain

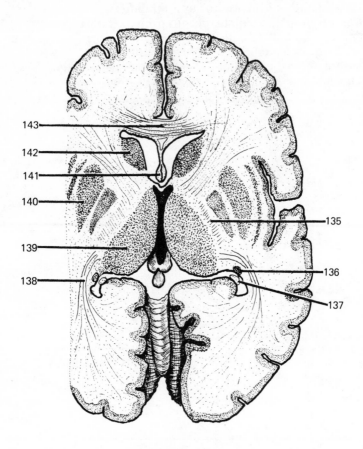

143
142
141
140
139
138
135
136
137

Identify the numbered structures, from the choices given below:

A	Thalamus	F	Head of caudate nucleus
B	Corpus callosum		
C	Optic radiation	G	Fornix, anterior pillar
D	Internal capsule	H	Fornix, posterior pillar
E	Hippocampus	J	Putamen
		K	Tail of caudate nucleus

Section of midbrain

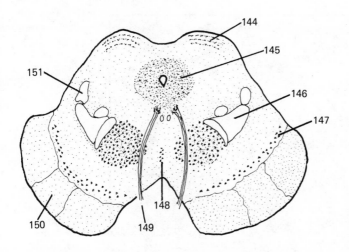

Identify the numbered structures, from the choices given below:

A	Superior colliculus	E	Substantia nigra
B	Oculomotor nerve	F	Medial lemniscus
C	Pyramidal tract	G	Periaqueductal grey
D	Raphe nucleus		matter
		H	Spinothalamic tract

Section of Pons

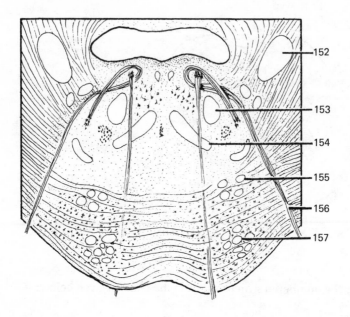

152
153
154
155
156
157

Identify the numbered structures, from the choices given below:

A   Central tegmental tract
B   Lateral lemniscus
C   Corticopontine fibres
D   Corticospinal fibres

E   Superior cerebellar peduncle
F   Medial lemniscus
G   Facial nerve
H   Abducent nerve

Section of spinal cord

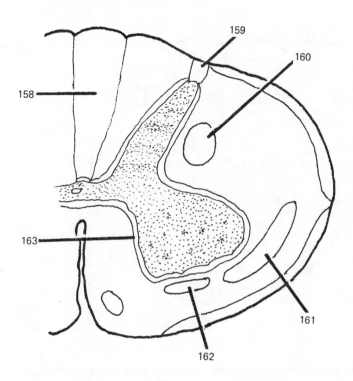

Identify the numbered structures, from the choices given below:

A   Fasciculus gracilis   E   Vestibulospinal tract
B   Fasciculus cuneatus   F   Propriospinal tract
C   Lissauer's tract   G   Spinothalamic
D   Rubrospinal tract   H   Lateral corticospinal
                                       tract

Neurone

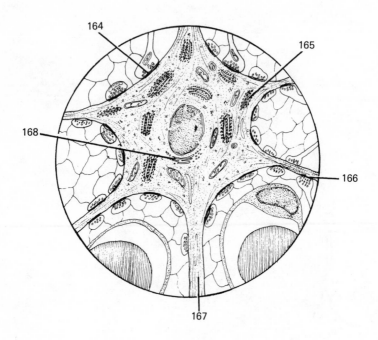

Identify the numbered structures, from the choices given below:

A   Axosomatic synapse   D   Dendrite
B   Nissl body   E   Golgi complex
C   Axodendritic synapse   F   Axon

Section of a nerve

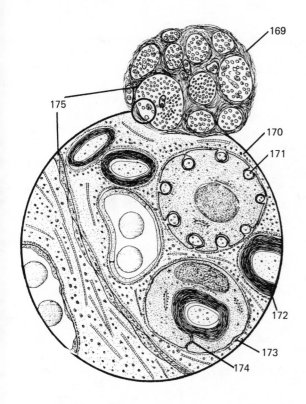

Identify the numbered structures, from the choices given below:

A	Epineurium	E	Basement membrane
B	Perineurium	F	Capillary endothelium
C	Endoneurium	G	Unmyelinated axon
D	Myelin sheath	H	Mesaxon

Motor end plate

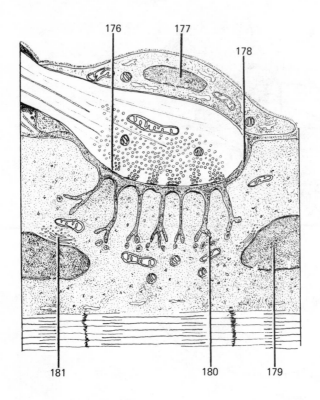

Identify the numbered structures, from the choices given below:

A	Golgi complex	E	Endomysium
B	Basement membrane	F	Active zone
C	Nucleus of Schwann cell	G	Junctional fold
D	Sole plate nucleus	H	Sarcomere

Answers

1.	C	43.	D	83.	E
2.	B	44.	C	84.	C
3.	C	45.	A	85.	C
4.	C	46.	A	86.	B
5.	B	47.	D	87.	B
6.	B	48.	A	88.	E
7.	A	49.	D	89.	B
8.	E	50.	D	90.	A
9.	A			91.	D
10.	D	51.	B	92.	E
11.	D	52.	B	93.	A
12.	E	53.	A	94.	A
13.	B	54.	A		
14.	E	55.	A	95.	A
15.	E	56.	C	96.	E
16.	A	57.	D	97.	B
17.	C	58.	B	98.	D
18.	E	59.	D	99.	C
19.	A	60.	D	100.	A
20.	D	61.	B	101.	B
21.	E	62.	D	102.	E
22.	A	63.	A	103.	D
23.	C	64.	C	104.	C
24.	E	65.	A	105.	B
25.	B	66.	D	106.	C
26.	B	67.	B	107.	A
27.	C	68.	B	108.	E
28.	C	69.	C	109.	D
29.	A	70.	C		
30.	A	71.	A	110.	T
31.	C	72.	A	111.	T
32.	C	73.	B	112.	T
33.	D	74.	B	113.	T
34.	C	75.	D	114.	T
35.	B	76.	A	115.	T
36.	C			116.	T
37.	B	77.	D	117.	T
38.	D	78.	E	118.	T
39.	C	79.	A	119.	T
40.	B	80.	A	120.	T
41.	B	81.	B	121.	T
42.	B	82.	A	122.	F

123. F	144. A	163. F
124. F	145. G	
125. T	146. F	164. A
126. F	147. E	165. B
127. T	148. D	166. C
128. T	149. B	167. F
129. F	150. C	168. E
130. T	151. H	
131. T		169. A
132. T		170. C
133. F	152. E	171. G
134. F	153. A	172. D
	154. F	173. E
	155. C	174. H
135. D	156. G	175. B
136. K	157. D	
137. H		
138. C		176. F
139. A	158. A	177. C
140. J	159. C	178. B
141. G	160. H	179. D
142. F	161. G	180. G
143. B	162. E	181. A

VIII HISTOLOGY

Questions 1–28

For each of the following multiple choice questions select the *one* most appropriate answer

1. **Nissl bodies are composed of:**
    - A Granular endoplasmic reticulum
    - B Smooth endoplasmic reticulum
    - C Golgi complexes
    - D Neurofilaments
    - E Microtubules

2. **Cilia are found in the epithelium of:**
    - A Maxillary air sinuses
    - B Bronchi
    - C Uterine tube
    - D All the above
    - E A and B only

3. **Stratified squamous epithelium lines:**
    - A Trachea
    - B Colon
    - C Rectum
    - D Ureter
    - E None of the above

4. **Simple squamous epithelium:**
   A   Is protective rather than secretory or absorptive
   B   Consists of a single layer of flattened cells
   C   Is not readily penetrated by water and ions
   D   Is keratinized in the oesophagus
   E   Has a rich supply of capillaries running between its cell layers

5. **The fibroblast:**
   A   Has little rough endoplasmic reticulum
   B   Is not an active cell
   C   Produces all the elastin in the body
   D   Is the second commonest cell in ordinary connective tissue
   E   Is mesodermal in origin

6. **Elastic fibres are found in the walls of:**
   A   Bronchi
   B   Bronchioles
   C   Pulmonary alveoli
   D   All the above
   E   None of the above

7. **Epiphyseal ossification centre always present at full term:**
   A   Proximal humerus
   B   Proximal fibula
   C   Distal femur
   D   Proximal tibia
   E   Distal tibia

8. **In synovial joints the synovial membrane:**
   A   Lines the inner surface of the capsule
   B   Covers the articular cartilage
   C   Does not cover intra-articular tendons
   D   Never communicates with adjacent synovial bursae
   E   None of the above

9. **Cardiac muscle:**
    A   Is richly innervated
    B   Is syncytial
    C   Is relatively avascular
    D   Has intercalated discs uniting the cells
    E   Has few mitochondria

10. **Smooth muscle is found in the wall of the:**
    A   Pharynx
    B   Upper end of oesophagus
    C   Lower end of oesophagus
    D   All the above
    E   Two of the above

11. **A peripheral nerve (e.g. ulnar):**
    A   Is enclosed in epineurium
    B   Is entirely motor
    C   Is devoid of myelination
    D   Contains microglia
    E   Is endodermal in origin

12. **The dorsal root ganglion:**
    A   Is a collection of cells within the brain stem
    B   Contains multipolar neurons
    C   Contains unipolar neurons
    D   Consists of efferent neurons
    E   Is associated with innervation of the dorsal part of
        the body wall only

13. **Conducting tissue in the heart is composed of:**
    A   Connective tissue
    B   Modified nerves
    C   Modified heart muscle
    D   Smooth muscle
    E   Sinusoidal blood vessels

14. **Capillaries differ from arterioles in having:**
    A   Pavement endothelium
    B   Smooth muscle
    C   An adventitial coat
    D   Sympathetic nerve endings
    E   No tunica media

15. **Alveoli of lungs communicate *directly* with one another through:**
    A   Alveolar ducts
    B   Atria
    C   Respiratory bronchioles
    D   Alveolar sacs
    E   Alveolar pores

16. **In the respiratory system:**
    A   Bronchioles have no cartilage
    B   The trachea is encircled by hyaline cartilage
    C   The nasal cavity has a simple squamous epithelium
    D   The larynx is lined throughout by ciliated, pseudostratified columnar epithelium
    E   Maxillary sinuses contain olfactory cells in their lining epithelium

17. **In the lymphatic system:**
    A   Plasma cells produce heparin
    B   The thymus has a fine reticular fibre network
    C   Lymphatic capillaries are present only in intestinal villi
    D   The lymphocyte is an immunologically competent cell
    E   The thoracic duct has no valves

18. **The spleen:**
    A   Is essential to life
    B   Filters blood and lymph
    C   Contains no plasma cells
    D   Has germinal centres in its lymph nodules
    E   Has afferent lymphatics entering at its hilum

19. **Substances applied to the skin surface may enter the skin freely through:**
    A   Hair follicles
    B   Sweat glands
    C   Stratum corneum
    D   Palm of hand
    E   Glomus cells

20. **In skin:**
   A   Sweat glands are absent from the palm and sole
   B   The epidermis has no nerves
   C   Prickle cells are joined in such a way that cytoplasm flows from cell to cell
   D   Defence cells form nodules in the epidermis
   E   Sebaceous glands are affected by sex hormones

21. **The odontoblast produces:**
   A   Enamel
   B   Dentin
   C   Cementum
   D   Pulp
   E   Alveolar bone

22. **In the stomach, parietal (oxyntic) cells are found in the:**
   A   Fundus
   B   Body
   C   Pyloric canal
   D   Cardiac region
   E   A and B

23. **In the ureter, the lining epithelium is:**
   A   Transitional
   B   Cuboidal
   C   Ciliated columnar
   D   Stratified squamous
   E   None of the above

24. **The following are characteristic of the normal kidney:**
   A   Distal convoluted tubules longer than proximal
   B   Slit membranes between macula densa and juxta-glomerular apparatus
   C   Glomerulus has single arteriole
   D   Cuboidal epithelium in parietal layer of Bowman's capsule
   E   Podocytes in visceral layer of Bowman's capsule

25. **Secretory granules in neurohypophysis acumulate in:**
   A   Pituicytes
   B   Nerve endings
   C   Intercellular spaces
   D   Sinusoids
   E   Capillary endothelium

26. **All endocrine tissue shows the following feature:**
   A   A rich capillary supply
   B   Encapsulation
   C   No lymphatics
   D   No nerve fibres
   E   Intracellular secretory granules

27. **The following cells contact the basement membrane of the seminiferous tubule:**
   A   Spermatogonia and Sertoli cells
   B   Sertoli cells and Leydig cells
   C   Primary and secondary spermatocytes
   D   Spermatogonia and Leydig cells
   E   Spermatids

28. **The secretory phase of the menstrual cycle is associated with:**
   A   Doubling of thickness of endometrium
   B   Widening and wrinkling (sawtooth) of glands
   C   Active corpus luteum
   D   All of the above
   E   A and B only

Questions 29–140

The set of lettered headings below is followed by a list of numbered words or phrases. For each numbered word or phrase select the correct answer under:

   A   If the item is associated with A only
   B   If the item is associated with B only
   C   If the item is associated with both A and B
   D   If the item is associated with neither A nor B

A   Hydrolytic enzymes
B   Oxidative phosphorylation
C   Both
D   Neither

29.   Lysosomes
30.   Nucleolus
31.   Free ribosomes
32.   Mitochondria

A   Mitotic spindle
B   Protein for export
C   Both
D   Neither

33.   Golgi apparatus
34.   Rough endoplasmic reticulum
35.   Centrioles
36.   Microvilli

A   Ciliated columnar epithelium
B   Stratified squamous epithelium
C   Both
D   Neither

37.   Larynx
38.   Pulmonary alveoli
39.   Tongue
40.   Oesophagus

A   Stratified keratinized epithelium
B   Simple columnar epithelium
C   Both
D   Neither

41.   Epididymis
42.   Hard palate
43.   Cervix of uterus
44.   Anterior two-thirds of tongue

A   Collagen fibrils
B   Elastic fibres
C   Both
D   Neither

45. May double their length on being stretched
46. Branch freely
47. Have high resistance to tensile strain
48. Show marked periodicity at 64 nm intervals

A   Elastic fibres
B   Smooth muscle
C   Both
D   Neither

49. Abundant in tunica media of aorta
50. Abundant in tunica media of arterioles
51. Absent from capillaries
52. Absent from veins

A   Intervertebral disc
B   Skull suture
C   Both
D   Neither

53. Synovial joint
54. Secondary cartilaginous joint
55. Syndesmosis
56. Primary cartilaginous joint

A   Cartilage
B   Bone
C   Both
D   Neither

57. Rich blood supply
58. Excellent reparative power
59. Collagen in matrix
60. Ground substance rich in glycosaminoglycano

A   Dense-cored granules containing serotonin
B   Reticulocytes
C   Both
D   Neither

61. Neutrophils
62. Lymphocytes
63. Erythrocytes
64. Platelets

A   Transverse tubules
B   Sarcoplasmic reticulum
C   Both
D   Neither

65. Cardiac muscle
66. Skeletal muscle
67. Intestinal muscle
68. Arrector pili

A   Dendrites
B   Axons
C   Both
D   Neither

69. Neurofibrils
70. Nissl substance
71. Lysosomes
72. Mitochondria

A   Attachment plaques
B   Nexuses (gap junctions)
C   Both
D   Neither

73. Extensors of the toes
74. Uterine muscle (myometrium)
75. Sphincter pupillae
76. Detrusor muscle of urinary bladder

A   Motor end plate
B   Muscle spindle
C   Both
D   Neither

77. Smooth muscle
78. Nail bed
79. Dental pulp
80. Cardiac muscle

A   Lymphatic vessels
B   Veins
C   Both
D   Neither

81. Commence blindly
82. Valves are present
83. Lined by endothelium
84. Contain erythrocytes

A   Aorta
B   Arterioles
C   Both
D   Neither

85. Rich in elastic fibres
86. Mainly muscular
87. Lined by flat endothelium
88. Adventitial coat is present

A   Hyaline cartilage
B   Elastic fibres
C   Both
D   Neither

89. Alveolar duct
90. Bronchus
91. Bronchiole
92. Air sac

A   Clara cells
B   Alveolar macrophages
C   Both
D   Neither

93. Alveolar wall
94. Respiratory bronchioles
95. Trachea
96. Larynx

A   Palatine tonsil
B   Lingual tonsil
C   Both
D   Neither

97. Lymphatics
98. B-lymphocytes
99. No capsule
100. Lymph nodules

A   Keratinocytes
B   Sebaceous gland
C   Both
D   Neither

101. Gap junctions
102. Hair follicle
103. Stratum basale
104. Melanin

A   Epidermis
B   Dermis
C   Both
D   Neither

105. Origin from mesoderm
106. Contain(s) blood vessels
107. Produce(s) keratin
108. Contain(s) lymph vessels

152

A   Liver lobule
B   Liver acinus
C   Both
D   Neither

109. Blood flow converges on a central vein
110. Invested by a loose connective tissue capsule
111. Several are supplied from a single portal vein
112. Devoid of sinusoids

A   Gall bladder
B   Appendix
C   Both
D   Neither

113. Simple epithelium
114. Villi
115. Immunological function
116. Folded mucous membrane

A   Absorption
B   Basal infoldings in lining cells
C   Both
D   Neither

117. Proximal convoluted tubule
118. Distal convoluted tubule
119. Collecting ducts
120. Renal pelvis

A   Basement membrane
B   Capillary network
C   Both
D   Neither

121. Glomerulus
122. Visceral layer of Bowman's capsule
123. Renal papilla
124. Loop of Henle

A   Mineralocorticoids
B   Oxyphil cells
C   Both
D   Neither

125. Pineal
126. Parathyroid
127. Suprarenal cortex
128. Thyroid

A   Contains axon terminals
B   Rich in blood supply
C   Both
D   Neither

129. Posterior pituitary
130. Thyroid
131. Adrenal medulla
132. Parathyroid

A   Corpus luteum
B   Graafian follicle
C   Both
D   Neither

133. Menopause
134. Menstruation
135. Progesterone
136. Oestrogen

A   Trophoblast
B   Mucous glands
C   Both
D   Neither

137. Graafian follicle
138. Placental membrane (barrier)
139. Epididymis
140. Endocervix (uterine)

154

Questions 141–168

Directions: In the following series of questions, one or more of the four items is/are correct.

Answer A   if 1, 2 and 3 are correct
       B   if 1 and 3 are correct
       C   if 2 and 4 are correct
       D   if only 4 is correct
and   E   if all four are correct

141. **A double membrane is associated with:**
    1. The Golgi apparatus
    2. The nucleus
    3. Rough endoplasmic reticulum
    4. The mitochondrion

142. **Microvilli are found in epithelium of:**
    1. Gall bladder
    2. Proximal convoluted tubules of kidney
    3. Intestinal epithelium
    4. Oesophagus

143. **Ciliated pseudostratified columnar epithelium lines:**
    1. The respiratory portion of the respiratory system
    2. The descending colon
    3. The distal convoluted tubule of the kidney
    4. The trachea

144. **From stratified squamous to pseudostratified columnar with mucus-secreting cells:**
    1. Dorsal to ventral surface of tongue
    2. Exocervix to endocervix
    3. Rectum to anal canal
    4. Oral to nasal surface of palate

145. **Collagen fibres are the main connective tissue fibres in:**
    1. Tendon
    2. The supporting framework of the spleen
    3. Capsules of joints
    4. The blood-air barrier

146. **Elastic fibres are essential:**
    1. In the supporting framework of lymph nodes
    2. In the capsule (Glisson's) of the liver
    3. In the ligaments of the knee
    4. In the walls of the air sacs of the lung

147. **Articular cartilage is:**
    1. Elastic
    2. Permanent
    3. Covered by perichondrium
    4. Avascular

148. **Fracture of the neck of the femur:**
    1. Occurs often in the elderly
    2. Always heals well
    3. May require pinning
    4. Is usually extracapsular

149. **Smooth muscle:**
    1. Colon
    2. Pylorus
    3. Oviduct
    4. Papillary muscles

150. **Voluntary striated muscle:**
    1. Contains actin filaments
    2. Has branching cells
    3. Contains myosin filaments
    4. Is rich in lymphocytes

151. **Multipolar neurones:**
    1. Posterior root ganglion cells
    2. Olfactory cells
    3. Cells of adrenal medulla
    4. Anterior horn cells

152. **Origin from neural crest:**
1. Schwann cells
2. Neural tube
3. Melanocytes
4. Suprarenal cortex

153. **Capillaries are absent from:**
1. Epidermis
2. Cartilage
3. Cornea
4. Bone

154. **Thin tunica media:**
1. Carotid body
2. Carotid sinus
3. Arterioles
4. Small and medium veins

155. **Basement membrane:**
1. Insignificant in bronchi
2. Absent in blood-air barrier
3. Well innervated in sphenoidal sinuses
4. Prominent in tracheal mucosa

156. **In nasal mucous membrane:**
1. No goblet cells
2. Bipolar neurones
3. Simple squamous epithelium
4. Rich vascularization

157. **Involved in protection against antigens:**
1. Nasal mucosa
2. Tracheal mucous membrane
3. Bronchiolar mucous membrane
4. Laryngeal mucous membrane

158. **Contains T-lymphocytes:**
   1. Thymus
   2. Spleen
   3. Lymph node
   4. Lymph nodule

159. **Hair grows faster:**
   1. When cut
   2. When washed frequently
   3. In Eskimos
   4. In Summer

160. **Melanocytes are present in:**
   1. The germinal matrix of hair
   2. The nail matrix
   3. Stratum basale of epidermis
   4. Cells of sebaceous glands

161. **The tongue:**
   1. Contains voluntary muscle running in three directions
   2. Is divisible into an anterior papillary one-third, and a posterior tonsillar two-thirds
   3. Has both serous and mucous glands
   4. Has no autonomic nerve supply

162. **Submucous glands present in:**
   1. Oesophagus
   2. Appendix
   3. Duodenum
   4. Caecum

163. **Confined to renal cortex:**
   1. Proximal convoluted tubule
   2. Glomerulus
   3. Loop of Henle
   4. Distal convoluted tubule

164. **Lined by transitional epithelium:**
    1. Renal pelvis
    2. Ureter
    3. Urinary bladder
    4. Collecting ducts

165. **The cells that comprise the parenchyma of the parathyroid gland are the:**
    1. Principal (chief) cells
    2. Parafollicular cells
    3. Oxyphil cells
    4. Beta cells

166. **Role in blood pressure control:**
    1. Anterior pituitary
    2. Posterior pituitary
    3. Pars media of pituitary
    4. Suprarenal cortex

167. **Endocrine cells in the testis:**
    1. Sertoli
    2. Spermatogonia
    3. Spermatids
    4. Leydig

168. **Found in the perivitelline space:**
    1. First polar body
    2. Spermatozoa
    3. Extensions of granulosa cells
    4. Embryoblast

Questions 169–302

The group of questions below consists of numbered headings, followed by a list of lettered words or phrases. For each heading select the *one* word or phrase which is most closely related to it. *Note:* Each choice may be used *only once.*

169.	Granular endoplasmic reticulum	A	Cytoskeleton
170.	Smooth endoplasmic reticulum	B	Protein for cell metabolism
171.	Free ribosomes	C	Nuclear DNA
172.	Microfibrils	D	Protein for secretion
173.	Chromosomes	E	Metabolism of fat

174.	Lysosomes	A	Hydrolytic enzymes
175.	Mitochondria	B	Oxidative phosphorylation
176.	Zona occludens	C	Fused membranes
177.	Macula adherens	D	Desmosome
178.	Gap junction (nexus)	E	Rapid conduction

179.	Stratified squamous keratinized epithelium	A	Jejunum
180.	Stratified squamous non-keratinized epithelium	B	Oesophagus
		C	Gums/Gingivae
		D	Bladder
		E	Alveolar sacs
181.	Stratified transitional epithelium		
182.	Simple squamous epithelium		
183.	Simple columnar epithelium		

184.	Ciliated epithelium	A	Gaseous exchange
185.	Columnar epithelium with microvilli	B	Absorption
186.	Simple squamous epithelium	C	Protection
		D	Distension
187.	Stratified squamous epithelium	E	Removal of particulate matter
188.	Transitional epithelium		

189.	Lymphocytes	A	Reticular fibres
190.	Plasma cells	B	Heparin
191.	Mast cells	C	Phagocytic
192.	Histiocyte	D	Antibodies
193.	Fibroblasts	E	Very little cytoplasm

194. Appositional growth	A	Tensile strength
195. Collagen fibres	B	Articular surfaces
196. Elastic cartilage	C	Bone
197. Fibrocartilage	D	Pinna (of ear)
198. Hyaline cartilage	E	Intervertebral disc

199. Elastic cartilage	A	Epiphysis of femur
200. Hyaline cartilage	B	Epiglottis
201. Fibrocartilage	C	Pubic symphysis
202. Cancellous bone	D	Shaft of radius
203. Compact bone	E	Tracheal rings

204. Osteoblasts	A	Form organic matrix of bone
205. Osteoclasts	B	Resorb bone
206. Osteocytes	C	Composed of bony lamellae
207. Osteones	D	Are highly branched cells

208. Intercalated discs	A	Postural muscle
209. Intermediate filaments	B	Contractile unit
210. Abundant myoglobin	C	Stretch receptors
211. Sarcomere	D	Smooth muscle
212. Muscle spindles	E	Cardiac muscle

213. Smooth muscle	A	Poor blood supply
214. Myoepithelium	B	Central blunt-ended nucleus
215. Cardiac muscle	C	Wall of ileum
216. Tendon	D	Peripheral nuclei
217. Skeletal muscle	E	Exocrine glands

218. All leucocytes	A	Histiocytes
219. Monocytes	B	Work outside the bloodstream
220. Lymphocytes	C	Become plasma cells
221. Eosinophils	D	Graft rejection
222. T-lymphocytes	E	Allergic conditions

223.	Muscle spindles	A	Perikaryon
224.	Unipolar cells	B	Stretch receptors
225.	Bipolar cells	C	Dorsal root ganglia
226.	Multipolar cells	D	Olfactory neurons
227.	Neurofibrils	E	Autonomic ganglia

228.	Rough endoplasmic reticulum	A	Schwann cell
229.	Neurofilaments	B	Motor end plates
230.	Myelin	C	Axon
231.	Dendrites	D	Afferent impulses
232.	Synaptic vesicles	E	Nissl substance

233.	Intercalated discs	A	Pressure reduction
234.	Papillary muscles	B	Many valves
235.	Arterioles	C	Fenestrations
236.	Lymphatics	D	Gap junctions
237.	Capillaries	E	Purkinje fibres

238.	Conducting system	A	Capillaries
239.	Selective distribution	B	Subendocardium
240.	Valves	C	Arterioles
241.	Pericytes	D	Veins of limbs
242.	Pressure reduction	E	Medium arteries

243.	Clara cells	A	Squamous epithelium
244.	Dust cells	B	Extrapulmonary bronchi
245.	Type I pneumocytes	C	Respiratory bronchioles
246.	Type II pneumocytes	D	Surfactant
247.	Cartilage rings	E	Macrophages

248.	Trachea	A	Continuous cartilage plates
249.	Branch bronchi	B	No cartilage
250.	Bronchioles	C	Elastic cartilage
251.	Larynx	D	C-shaped cartilage rings
252.	Conchae	E	Erectile tissue

253.	Spleen	A	Cytotoxic lymphocytes
254.	Lymph node	B	Subcapsular sinus
255.	Thymus	C	Peyer's patches
256.	Ileum	D	Periarterial nodules
257.	Bursa of Fabricius	E	B-lymphocytes

258.	Lymphatic capillary	A	Medullary cords
259.	Lymph node	B	Cellular reticulum
260.	Tonsils	C	Simple valves
261.	Thymus	D	Anchoring filaments
262.	Thoracic duct	E	Partially encapsulated

263.	Lacteal	A	Hydrochloric acid
264.	Oxyntic cells	B	Digestive enzymes
265.	Zymogenic cells	C	Villus
266.	Striated muscle	D	Pylorus
267.	Mucous glands	E	Soft palate

268.	Chief cells	A	Canaliculi
269.	Parietal cells	B	Submucosal
270.	Brunner's glands	C	Mitotic figures
271.	Crypts of Lieberkühn	D	Colon
272.	Taeniae coli	E	Much rough endoplasmic reticulum

273.	Afferent arteriole	A	Macula densa
274.	Distal tubule	B	Juxtaglomerular apparatus
275.	Renal papilla	C	Minor calyx
276.	Medullary rays	D	Collecting tubules
277.	Continuous with Bowman's capsule	E	None of the above

278.	Mesangial cells	A	Fenestrated endothelium
279.	Afferent arteriole	B	Very thick
280.	Glomerular capillaries	C	Phagocytic
281.	Podocytes	D	Visceral epithelium of Bowman's capsule
282.	Glomerular basement membrane	E	Juxtaglomerular cells

283. Thyroid	A	Alpha cells
284. Adrenal medulla	B	Zona reticularis
285. Pancreas	C	Melanocyte stimulating
286. Adrenal cortex		hormone
287. Middle lobe of pituitary	D	Chromaffin cells
	E	Parafollicular cells

288. Suprarenal cortex	A	Progesterone
289. Suprarenal medulla	B	Cortisol
290. Adenohypophysis	C	Follicle stimulating
291. Neurohypophysis		hormone
292. Corpus luteum	D	Adrenaline
	E	Oxytocin

293. Cumulus oophorus	A	First polar body
294. Vitelline membrane	B	Granulosa cells
295. Perivitelline space	C	Embryoblast
296. Ampulla of oviduct	D	Plasmalemma
297. Inner cell mass	E	Site of fertilization

298. Stem cells	A	Proliferative
299. Corpus luteum		endometrium
300. Exocervix	B	Secretory phase of
301. Graafian follicle		cycle
302. Sperm head	C	Acrosome
	D	Spermatogonia
	E	Stratified squamous
		epithelium

Questions 303–417

In reply to the following questions, indicate whether you think each statement is *True* or *False*:

The cell membrane:
303. Consists of a lipid bilayer with protein associated with both surfaces
304. Is a barrier to the passage of lipid-soluble substances
305. Has a higher concentration of sodium ions on its outer than on its inner surface
306. Is not the same thing as the cell coat
307. Is about 9 μm thick

Smooth endoplasmic reticulum:
308. Detoxifies drugs
309. Synthesizes lipids
310. Stores glycogen
311. Contains calcium ions
312. Is studded with ribosomes

Keratinized epithelium:
313. Is always stratified
314. Covers the soft palate completely
315. Covers the ventral surface of the tongue
316. Lines the oesophagus
317. Forms the epidermis

Simple squamous epithelium:
318. Lines air sacs
319. Develops from all three germ layers
320. Is a protective epithelium
321. Is usually secretory
322. Lines all cavities of the cardiovascular system, where it is called endothelium

Adipose tissue:
323. Is derived from embryonic ectoderm
324. Has a rich blood supply
325. Has a sympathetic nerve supply
326. Is a good insulator
327. Can develop anywhere in the body where mesenchyme existed in the embryo

Tendon:
328. Is a type of dense connective tissue adapted to weight-bearing
329. Is primarily a cellular tissue with a protective function
330. Has dense bundles of collagen, all running in the same direction and causing the cells to be distributed in a linear manner
331. Has a rich blood supply
332. Cannot undergo repair if severed

Cartilage:
333. Is an avascular tissue
334. Never forms a permanent structure
335. Increases in amount by both appositional and interstitial growth
336. Cannot survive if invaded by blood capillaries
337. Is everywhere covered by perichondrium

Bone:
338. After fracture, remains permanently weaker
339. In the skull, is united to adjacent bones by syndesmoses
340. Of the limbs is developed from lateral plate mesoderm
341. When first formed is always cancellous
342. Is decalcified by cells rich in rough endoplasmic reticulum

Myeloid tissue:
343. Is present in the iliac crest
344. Contains progenitor cells for T-lymphocytes
345. Has a poor blood supply
346. Has a reticular fibre stroma
347. Contains megakarocytes

Smooth muscle cells:
348. Have a single nucleus located in the widest part of the cells
349. Contain myofilaments which are visible only with the electron microscope
350. Remain constant in size throughout life
351. Can be replaced by transformation of mesenchymal cells even in adult life
352. Form tight junctions with each other to aid in the transmission of waves of contraction

In cardiac muscle:
353. Peripheral nuclei are characteristic
354. Gap junctions join cells
355. A rich nerve supply is seen
356. Many mitochondria are required
357. No striations are visible

In peripheral nerves:
358. The endoneurium is interrupted at nodes of Ranvier
359. Schwann cell constitutes neurolemma
360. Perineurium encloses fascicles
361. The axolemma is the plasma membrane of an axon
362. There are no elastic fibres

In skin innervation:
363. Pacinian corpuscles are subcutaneous
364. Ruffini endings occupy the deep dermis
365. Meissner's corpuscles may contain up to nine axons
366. Myenteric plexuses are found near epidermal ridges
367. Follicular endings are applied to Merkel cells

In the cardiovascular system:
368. Veins can be distinguished from lymphatics by the absence of valves in the latter
369. Arterioles have a thick muscular media relative to the size of their lumina
370. Conducting tissue can be found in the subendocardium
371. Cardiac valves have a rich blood supply
372. In general the walls of veins are thinner than those of their companion arteries

In the circulatory system:
373. Arterioles control the amount of blood going to a particular region, e.g. the arm or the digestive system
374. Elastic laminae decrease in number in the aorta from birth onwards
375. Heart valves have a core of cardiac muscle
376. Veins have thick walls in relation to the size of the lumen of the vessel
377. Capillaries have no basement membrane

In the respiratory system:
378. The extrapulmonary subdivisions of the trachea have cartilage in their walls
379. The basement membrane is unusually prominent in the mucous membrane of the conducting portion of the system
380. Elastic tissue is not a feature of the conducting portion of the system
381. The paranasal air sinuses have abundant goblet cells in their epithelial lining
382. Respiratory bronchioles are directly associated with air sacs

In lymphatic tissue:
383. The thymus has no lymphocytes at birth
384. The thymus does not produce plasma cells
385. The spleen can be identified by the presence of Hassal's corpuscles
386. The spleen filters lymph
387. Nodules in lamina propria are encapsulated

Plasma cells:
388. Produce heparin and histamine
389. Participate in the immune response
390. Are found in abundance beneath wet epithelial surfaces
391. Are absent from connective tissue underlying respiratory epithelium
392. Are present in lymph nodes

In the intestine:
393. The appendix has abundant lymphatic tissue
394. There are no crypts of Lieberkühn in the colon
395. There are no microvilli in the jejunum
396. There are no taeniae in the ileum
397. There is a nerve plexus between the layers of the muscularis externa in the duodenum

In the kidney:
398. Podocytes line collecting ducts
399. The pelvis of the ureter is lined by transitional epithelium
400. Collecting ducts, stimulated by antidiuretic hormone, resorb fluid
401. All renal corpuscles are in the cortex
402. Interlobar arteries are end arteries

Parathyroid gland:
403. Contains chief cells which produce parathyroid hormone
404. Parathormone elevates serum calcium
405. Co-operates with the thyroid to control blood calcium levels
406. Diminishes renal tubular absorption of calcium
407. Lies outside the true capsule of the thyroid

The adrenal gland:
408. Cortex is of mesodermal origin
409. Medulla is ectodermal
410. Has three zones in the medulla
411. Cortex has poor blood supply
412. Medullary cells are modified sympathetic neurons

The mammary gland:
413. Contains about 20 compound exocrine glands
414. Pubertal increase in size is mainly due to adipose tissue
415. Secretes milk in response to adrenal cortical stimulation
416. Has lactiferous ducts lined by a double layer of columnar cells
417. Has myoepithelial cells surrounding the secretory units

Developing bone

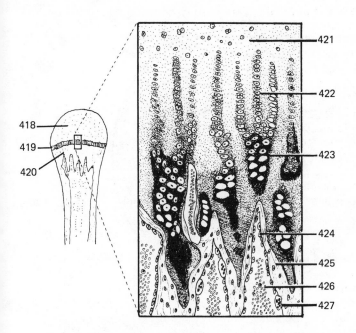

Identify the numbered structures, from the choices given below:

A   Osteoclast
B   Epiphyseal plate
C   Zone of proliferating
    cartilage
D   Epiphysis
E   Osteoblast
F   Nerve
G   Diaphysis

H   Myeloid tissue
J   Zone of calcified
    cartilage
K   Zone of maturing
    cartilage
L   Metaphysis
M   Artery
N   Trabeculum
O   Fibrocartilage

Intervertebral disc

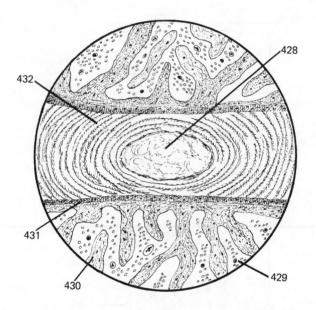

Identify the numbered structures, from the choices given below:

A	Cortical bone	E	Nucleus pulposus
B	Trabeculated bone	F	Hyaline cartilage
C	Nerve	G	Myeloid tissue
D	Annulus fibrosus	H	Tendon

Larynx

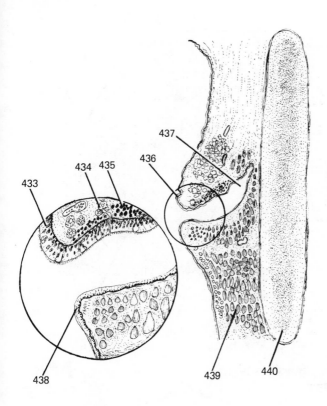

Identify the numbered structures, from the choices given below:

A   Lymphoid tissue
B   Stratified squamous
      epithelium
C   Vocal fold
D   Vestibular fold
E   Thyroid cartilage

F   Ciliated columnar
      epithelium
G   Thyroid gland
H   Saccule
J   Striated muscle
K   Mucous gland

Lung

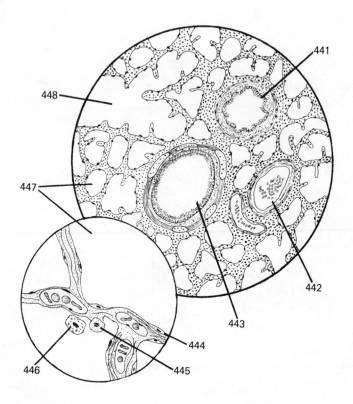

Identify the numbered structures, from the choices given below:

A	Alveolus	G	Bronchiole
B	Branch of pulmonary artery	H	Capillary
		J	Type I pneumocyte
C	Tracheal ring	K	Type II pneumocyte
D	Alveolar duct	L	Main bronchus
E	Branch bronchus	M	Macrophage
F	Alveolar sac		

Spleen

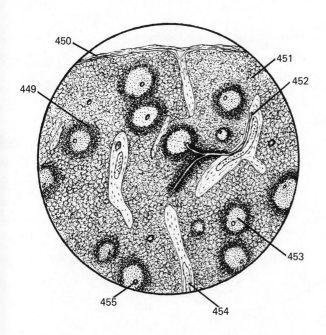

Identify the numbered structures, from the choices given below:

A	Central artery	F	Trabecular artery
B	Subcapsular sinus	G	Hassal's corpuscle
C	Trabecular vein	H	Capsule
D	Germinal centre	J	Red pulp
E	Marginal zone	K	White pulp

Developing tooth

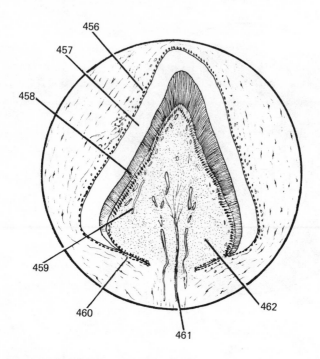

456
457
458
459
460
461
462

Identify the numbered structures, from the choices given below:

A   Dentin
B   Ameloblasts
C   Enamel space
D   Nerve
E   Pulp

F   Odontoblasts
G   Lymphatic vessel
H   Cementocytes
J   Bone
K   Epithelial diaphragm

Stomach

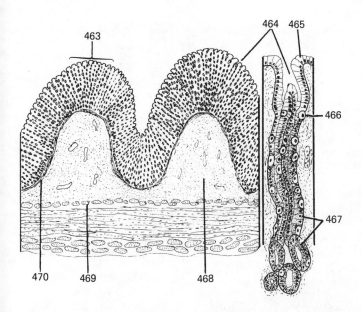

Identify the numbered structures, from the choices given below:

A	Gastric pit	G	Inner oblique muscle
B	Auerbach's plexus	H	Mucous cell
C	Ruga	J	Muscularis mucosae
D	Parietal (oxyntic) cells	K	Meissner's plexus
E	Chief (zymogenic) cells	L	Villus
F	Submucosa	M	Lacteal

Duodenum

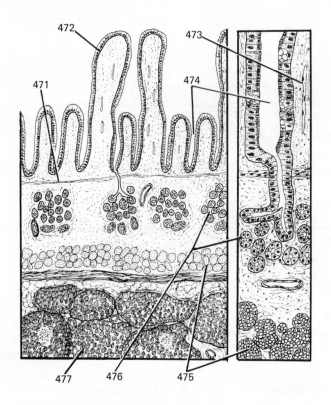

Identify the numbered structures, from the choices given below:

A	Muscularis mucosae	F	Lacteal
B	Muscularis externa	G	Wirsung's duct
C	Brünner's glands	H	Crypt of Lieberkühn
D	Pancreas	J	Enteroendocrine cells
E	Villus	K	Islets of Langerhans

Pancreas

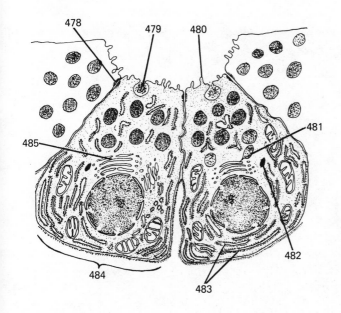

Identify the numbered structures, from the choices given below:

A   Rough endoplasmic
    reticulum
B   Smooth endoplasmic
    reticulum
C   Microvillus
D   Junctional complex
E   Centriole

F   Golgi complex
G   Forming vesicle
H   Lysome
J   Acinar cell
K   Zymogen granules

Vermiform appendix

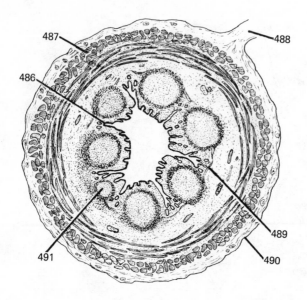

Identify the numbered structures, from the choices given below:

A	Mesentery	E	Peyer's patch
B	Crypt	F	Germinal centre
C	Serosa	G	Muscularis mucosae
D	Lacteal	H	Longitudinal muscle

Kidney

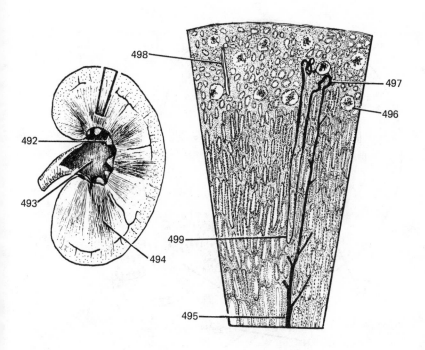

Identify the numbered structures, from the choices given below:

A	Papilla	G	Interlobar artery
B	Minor calyx	H	Distal convoluted
C	Renal vein		tubule
D	Renal pelvis	J	Collecting duct
E	Loop of Henle	K	Interlobular artery
F	Pyramid	L	Renal corpuscle
		M	Arcuate artery

Ureter

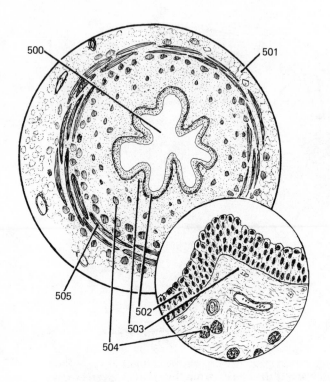

Identify the numbered structures, from the choices given below:

A Transitional epithelium
B Lamina propria
C Circular muscle
D Vein

E Adventitia
F Longitudinal muscle
G Meissner's plexus
H Stellate lumen

Ovary

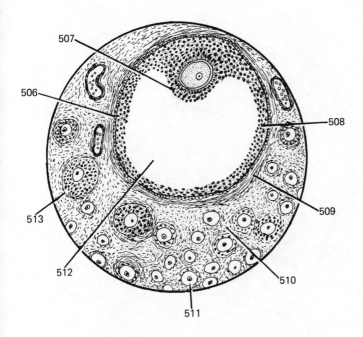

Identify the numbered structures, from the choices given below:

A	Granulosa cells (follicular)	F	Theca interna
B	Primary oocyte	G	Theca externa
C	Stroma	H	Sertoli cells
D	Antrum	J	Secondary follicle
E	Cumulus oophorus	K	Capsule

Thyroid gland

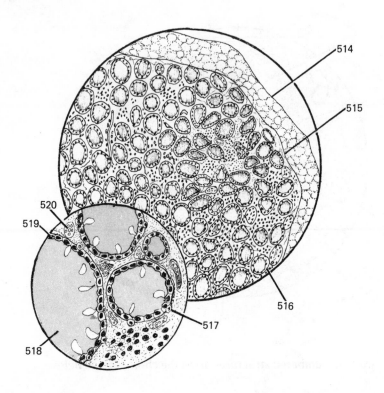

Identify the numbered structures, from the choices given below:

A	Colloid	F	Lymphatic tissue
B	Septa	G	Pretracheal fascia
C	Follicle	H	Blood vessel
D	True capsule	J	Parafollicular cell
E	Cuboidal epithelium		

Adrenal gland

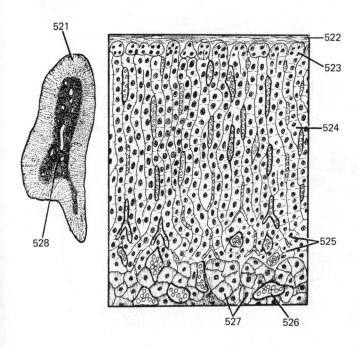

Identify the numbered structures, from the choices given below:

A   Chromaffin cells   F   Capsule
B   Zona reticularis   G   Islets
C   Medulla   H   Blood vessel
D   Secretory veiscles   J   Cortex
E   Zona glomerulosa   K   Zona fasciculata

Skin

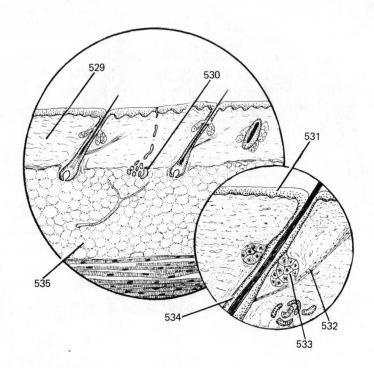

Identify the numbered structures, from the choices given below:

A   Sweat gland
B   Dermis
C   Striated muscle
D   Pacinian corpuscle
E   Sebaceous gland

F   Arrector pili
G   Hypodermis
H   External root sheath
J   Epidermis

Lactating breast

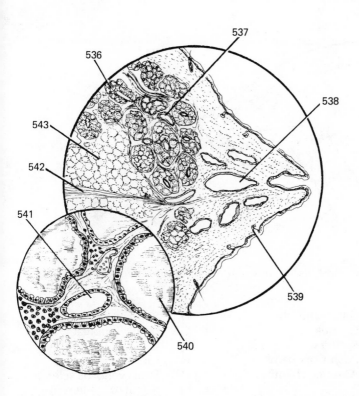

Identify the numbered structures, from the choices given below:

A	Intralobular duct	F	Alveoli
B	Suspensory ligament	G	Fat
C	Lactiferous sinus	H	Pectoralis major
D	Secretion	J	Pectoral fascia
E	Intralobar duct	K	Sweat gland

Anterior part of eye

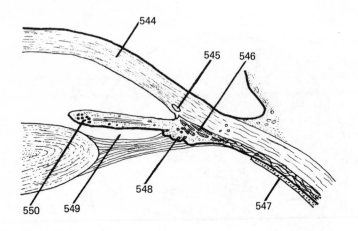

Identify the numbered structures, from the choices given below:

A	Ciliary muscle	F	Sphincter pupillae
B	Cornea	G	Dilator pupillae
C	Retina	H	Lens
D	Posterior chamber	J	Ciliary process
E	Anterior chamber	K	Sinus venosus sclerae (canal of Schlemm)

Cochlea

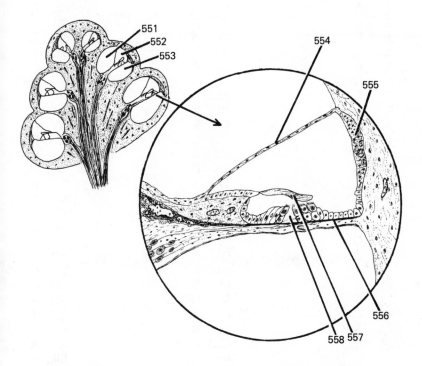

Identify the numbered structures, from the choices given below:

A Scala vestibuli   E Stria vascularis
B Scala tympani   F Tectorial membrane
C Cochlea duct   G Vestibular membrane
D Basilar membrane   H Tunnel of Corti

Answers

1.	A	42.	A	84.	B
2.	D	43.	B	85.	A
3.	E	44.	A	86.	B
4.	B	45.	B	87.	C
5.	E	46.	B	88.	C
6.	D	47.	A	89.	B
7.	C	48.	A	90.	C
8.	A	49.	A	91.	B
9.	D	50.	B	92.	B
10.	C	51.	C	93.	B
11.	A	52.	D	94.	A
12.	C	53.	D	95.	D
13.	C	54.	A	96.	D
14.	E	55.	B	97.	D
15.	E	56.	D	98.	C
16.	A	57.	B	99.	B
17.	D	58.	B	100.	C
18.	D	59.	C	101.	D
19.	A	60.	C	102.	C
20.	E	61.	D	103.	C
21.	B	62.	D	104.	A
22.	E	63.	B	105.	B
23.	A	64.	A	106.	B
24.	E	65.	C	107.	A
25.	B	66.	C	108.	B
26.	A	67.	B	109.	A
27.	A	68.	B	110.	A
28.	D	69.	C	111.	C
		70.	A	112.	D
29.	A	71.	D	113.	C
30.	D	72.	C	114.	D
31.	D	73.	D	115.	B
32.	B	74.	C	116.	A
33.	B	75.	C	117.	C
34.	B	76.	C	118.	C
35.	A	77.	D	119.	A
36.	D	78.	D	120.	D
37.	C	79.	D	121.	C
38.	D	80.	D	122.	C
39.	B	81.	A	123.	A
40.	B	82.	C	124.	C
41.	B	83.	C	125.	D

126. B	169. D	213. C
127. A	170. E	214. E
128. D	171. B	215. B
129. C	172. A	216. A
130. C	173. C	217. D
131. C	174. A	218. B
132. C	175. B	219. A
133. D	176. C	220. C
134. D	177. D	221. E
135. A	178. E	222. D
136. C	179. C	223. B
137. B	180. B	224. C
138. A	181. D	225. D
139. D	182. E	226. E
140. B	183. A	227. A
	184. E	228. E
141. C	185. B	229. C
142. A	186. A	230. A
143. D	187. C	231. D
144. C	188. D	232. B
145. B	189. E	233. D
146. D	190. D	234. E
147. C	191. B	235. A
148. B	192. C	236. B
149. A	193. A	237. C
150. B	194. C	238. B
151. D	195. A	239. E
152. B	196. D	240. D
153. A	197. E	241. A
154. C	198. B	242. C
155. D	199. B	243. C
156. C	200. E	244. E
157. E	201. C	245. A
158. E	202. A	246. D
159. D	203. D	247. B
160. B	204. A	248. D
161. B	205. B	249. A
162. B	206. D	250. B
163. C	207. C	251. C
164. A	208. E	252. E
165. B	209. D	253. D
166. C	210. A	254. B
167. D	211. B	255. A
168. A	212. C	256. C

257. E	301. A	344. T
258. D	302. C	345. F
259. A		346. T
260. E	303. T	347. T
261. B	304. F	348. T
262. C	305. T	349. T
263. C	306. T	350. F
264. A	307. F	351. T
265. B	308. T	352. F
266. E	309. T	353. F
267. D	310. T	354. T
268. E	311. T	355. F
269. A	312. F	356. T
270. B	313. T	357. F
271. C	314. F	358. F
272. D	315. F	359. T
273. B	316. F	360. T
274. A	317. T	361. T
275. C	318. T	362. F
276. D	319. T	363. T
277. E	320. F	364. T
278. C	321. F	365. T
279. E	322. T	366. F
280. A	323. F	367. F
281. D	324. T	368. F
282. B	325. T	369. T
283. E	326. T	·370. T
284. D	327. F	371. F
285. A	328. F	372. T
286. B	329. F	373. F
287. C	330. T	374. F
288. B	331. F	375. F
289. D	332. F	376. F
290. C	333. T	377. F
291. E	334. F	378. T
292. A	335. T	379. T
293. B	336. T	380. F
294. D	337. F	381. F
295. A	338. F	382. T
296. E	339. T	383. F
297. C	340. T	384. T
298. D	341. T	385. F
299. B	342. F	386. F
300. E	343. T	387. F

388. F	430. B	468. F
389. T	431. F	469. G
390. T	432. D	470. J
391. F		
392. T	433. F	471. A
393. T	434. K	472. E
394. F	435. A	473. F
395. F	436. D	474. H
396. T	437. H	475. B
397. T	438. B	476. C
398. F	439. J	477. D
399. T	440. E	
400. T		478. D
401. T	441. G	479. K
402. T	442. B	480. C
403. T	443. E	481. G
404. T	444. J	482. H
405. T	445. K	483. A
406. T	446. M	484. J
407. T	447. A	485. F
408. T	448. D	
409. T		486. B
410. F	449. E	487. H
411. F	450. H	488. A
412. T	451. J	489. G
413. T	452. F	490. C
414. T	453. D	491. F
415. F	454. C	
416. T	455. A	492. A
417. T		493. D
	456. B	494. F
418. D	457. C	495. J
419. B	458. A	496. L
420. L	459. G	497. H
421. K	460. K	498. K
422. C	461. D	499. E
423. J	462. E	
424. E		500. H
425. N	463. C	501. E
426. H	464. A	502. A
427. A	465. H	503. B
	466. D	504. F
428. E	467. E	505. C
429. G		

506.	F	524.	K	542.	B
507.	E	525.	B	543.	G
508.	A	526.	H		
509.	G	527.	A	544.	B
510.	C	528.	C	545.	K
511.	B			546.	A
512.	D	529.	B	547.	C
513.	J	530.	A	548.	J
		531.	J	549.	D
514.	G	532.	F	550.	F
515.	D	533.	E		
516.	C	534.	H	551.	A
517.	J	535.	G	552.	C
518.	A			553.	B
519.	E	536.	F	554.	G
520.	H	537.	E	555.	E
		538.	C	556.	D
521.	J	539.	K	557.	F
522.	F	540.	D	558.	H
523.	E	541.	A		

IX EMBRYOLOGY

Questions 1–37

For each of the following multiple choice questions select the *one* most appropriate answer:

1.   **The chromosomal formula of the normal human ovum is:**
   A   44 autosomes and 2 X chromosomes
   B   45 autosomes and 1 X chromosome
   C   22 autosomes and 1 Y chromosome
   D   22 autosomes and 1 X chromosome
   E   44 autosomes and 2 Y chromosomes

2.   **Following ovulation the ovum is viable for up to:**
   A   One hour
   B   Twenty-four hours
   C   Three days
   D   Four days
   E   Seven days

3.   **The ovum is surrounded by a non-cellular, secreted layer known as the:**
   A   Corona radiata
   B   Theca folliculi
   C   Zona pellucida
   D   Cumulus oophorus
   E   Stratum granulosum

4.   The spermatozoon is usually viable within the female genital
     tract for up to:
     A   One hour
     B   Twenty-four hours
     C   Forty-eight hours
     D   Four days
     E   Seven days

5.   The usual number of days between fertilization and the
     commencement of implantation is:
     A   One
     B   Three
     C   Six
     D   Ten
     E   Fourteen

6.   The fertilized ovum is completely implanted in the
     endometrium by the end of the — day after fertilization:
     A   Third
     B   Seventh
     C   Fourteenth
     D   Twenty-first
     E   Twenty-eighth

7.   *Fraternal* twins may arise by:
     A   Simultaneous fertilization of two ova
     B   Division of a single fertilized ovum
     C   Duplication of the embryoblast
     D   Duplication of the primitive streak
     E   All of the above mechanisms

8.   The uterine cavity is obliterated during pregnancy by fusion
     of:
     A   Chorion frondosum and decidua basalis
     B   Decidua capsularis and decidua parietalis
     C   Amnion and decidua capsularis
     D   Amnion and chorion
     E   Endometrium and myometrium

9. **The embryo is called a fetus after the:**
    A   Third week
    B   Eighth week
    C   Twelfth week
    D   Sixteenth week
    E   Twenty-eighth week

10. **At the rostral end of the primitive streak lies the primitive:**
    A   Spot
    B   Node
    C   Notochord
    D   Plate
    E   Groove

11. **At the caudal end of the primitive steak, ectoderm and endoderm meet at the:**
    A   Notochordal canal
    B   Coelom
    C   Cloacal membrane
    D   Neural groove
    E   Notochord

12. **The neural crest separates off from the:**
    A   Neural groove
    B   Neural fold
    C   Neural tube
    D   Neurenteric canal
    E   Neuropore

13. **Segmentation is observed in the — mesoderm:**
    A   Paraxial
    B   Intermediate
    C   Lateral plate
    D   Splanchnic
    E   Branchial

14. **The embryonic coelom is formed between the layers of the:**
    A   Ectoderm
    B   Mesoderm
    C   Endoderm
    D   Somatopleure
    E   Splanchnopleure

15. **The mesenchymal vertebrae are formed from:**
    A   Sclerotomes
    B   Myotomes
    C   Dermatomes
    D   Notochord
    E   Cartilage rudiments

16. **At birth, the normal umbilical cord contains:**
    A   Two umbilical veins
    B   The vitelline duct
    C   The ductus venosus
    D   Two umbilical arteries
    E   The allantois

17. **The oral (buccopharyngeal) membrane separates:**
    A   Amniotic sac from yolk sac
    B   Nasal cavity from oral cavity
    C   Proctodeum from hindgut
    D   Larynx from pharynx
    E   Stomodeum from foregut

18. **The urorectal septum divides the cloaca into:**
    A   Rectum and urogenital sinus
    B   Rectum and bladder
    C   Bladder and allantois
    D   Hindgut and bladder
    E   Urethra and anal canal

19. **The cloaca of the embryo contributes to the:**
    A   Bladder
    B   Ureter
    C   Descending colon
    D   Permanent kidney
    E   Spinal cord

20. **The conus regions of both cardiac ventricles are derived from:**
    A   Sinus venosus
    B   Primitive atrium
    C   Primitive ventricle
    D   Bulbus cordis
    E   Truncus arteriosus

21. **Ductus venosus connects:**
    A   Umbilical vein to sinus venosus
    B   Right to left umbilical vein
    C   Pulmonary trunk to aorta
    D   Right to left atrium
    E   Hepatic veins to inferior vena cava

22. **The ligamentum arteriosum is derived from the:**
    A   Ductus arteriosus
    B   Glomus arteriosus
    C   Conus arteriosus
    D   Truncus arteriosus
    E   Umbilical artery

23. **The inguinal canal is created by:**
    A   Gubernaculum of gonad
    B   Processus vaginalis
    C   Descent of the gonad
    D   Spermatic cord
    E   External spermatic fascia

24. **The mesonephric duct persists as the:**
    A   Uterine tube
    B   Round ligament of uterus
    C   Ureter
    D   Ductus (vas) deferens
    E   Nephrons

25. **The mesonephros is the permanent kidney of:**
    A   Fishes
    B   Amphibia
    C   All mammals
    D   Primates only
    E   Man only

26. **Derived from the vitelline duct:**
   A   Ductus venosus
   B   Portal vein
   C   Gall bladder
   D   Duodenum
   E   Meckel's diverticulum

27. **The two embryonic portions of the permanent human kidney are:**
   A   Mesonephros and metanephros
   B   Mesonephric duct and metanephros
   C   Metanephric cap and mesonephric duct
   D   Metanephric cap and ureteric diverticulum
   E   Ureteric diverticulum and nephrogenic cord

28. **The commonest malformation of the kidney is:**
   A   Horseshoe kidney
   B   Congenital cystic kidney
   C   Partial duplication
   D   Unilateral agenesis
   E   Failure of ascent

29. **An ectopic testis may be found in the:**
   A   Pelvis
   B   Superficial inguinal ring
   C   Inguinal canal
   D   Scrotum
   E   Perineum

30. **Origin from second (hyoid) branchial arch:**
   A   Trapezius
   B   Temporalis
   C   Occipitofrontalis
   D   Lingual musculature
   E   Lower teeth

31. **The premaxilla is formed from the:**
   - A   Medial nasal processes
   - B   The maxillary processes
   - C   The lingual swellings
   - D   The mandibular arch
   - E   The nasal septum

32. **Bone ossified from a cartilaginous precursor:**
   - A   Frontal
   - B   Parietal
   - C   Zygomatic
   - D   Maxilla
   - E   None of the above

33. **The sulcus limitans of the developing neural tube separates:**
   - A   Alar lamina from basal lamina
   - B   The alar laminae
   - C   The basal laminae
   - D   Ependymal layer from mantle layer
   - E   Mantle layer from marginal layer

34. **The cephalic flexure of the brain occurs in the region of:**
   - A   Medulla oblongata
   - B   Pons
   - C   Midbrain
   - D   Diencephalon
   - E   Telencephalon

35. **The somatic efferent cell column of the primitive neural tube occupies the:**
   - A   Roof plate
   - B   Floor plate
   - C   Alar lamina
   - D   Basal lamina
   - E   Marginal layer

36. **Developmentally, the corpus striatum belongs to the:**
    A Telencephalon
    B Diencephalon
    C Mesencephalon
    D Metencephalon
    E Myelencephalon

37. **The last descending tract to undergo myelination:**
    A Rubrospinal
    B Tectospinal
    C Olivospinal
    D Corticospinal
    E Reticulospinal

Questions 38–46

The set of lettered headings below is followed by a list of numbered words or phrases. For each numbered word or phrase select the correct answer under:

    A If the item is associated with A only
    B If the item is associated with B only
    C If the item is associated with both A and B
    D If the item is associated with neither A nor B

    A Oxygenated blood
    B Reduced blood
    C Both
    D Neither

38. Ductus venosus
39. Umbilical vein
40. Umbilical artery
41. Vitelline duct

A   Ventral mesogastrium
B   Dorsal mesogastrium
C   Both
D   Neither

42. Lesser omentum
43. Greater omentum
44. Falciform ligament
45. Gastrosplenic ligament
46. Lienorenal ligament

Questions 47–63

Directions: In the following series of questions, one or more of the four items is/are correct.

Answer A   if 1, 2 and 3 are correct
       B   if 1 and 3 are correct
       C   if 2 and 4 are correct
       D   if only 4 is correct
and   E   if all four are correct

47. **Component(s) of a tertiary chorionic villus:**
    1.   Amniotic epithelium
    2.   Fetal vessels
    3.   Lacunae
    4.   Trophoblast

48. **The following structure(s) separate(s) fetal from maternal blood in the mature placenta:**
    1.   Fetal capillary endothelium
    2.   Maternal capillary endothelium
    3.   Syncytiotrophoblast
    4.   Lamina densa

49. **Component(s) of the oral membrane:**
    1.   Ectoderm
    2.   Mesoderm
    3.   Endoderm
    4.   Notochord

50. **Derived from the cloaca:**
   1. Rectum
   2. Bladder
   3. Urethra
   4. Allantois

51. **Derived from septum transversum:**
   1. Musculature of diaphragm
   2. Central tendon of diaphragm
   3. Transverse sinus of pericardium
   4. Connective tissue of liver

52. **Derived from sinus venosus:**
   1. Sinus venarum
   2. Left atrium
   3. Coronary sinus
   4. Superior vena cava

53. **Derived from truncus arteriosus:**
   1. Pulmonary trunk
   2. Coronary arteries
   3. Ascending aorta
   4. Ductus arteriosus

54. **Organ(s) developing from two primordia:**
   1. Stomach
   2. Pancreas
   3. Appendix
   4. Definitive kidney (metanephros)

55. **The developing diaphragm receives contributions from the:**
   1. Septum transversum
   2. Ventral mesogastrium
   3. Pleuroperitoneal membranes
   4. Dorsal mesocardium

56. **The foregut of the embryo gives rise to the:**
   1. Anterior lobe of hypophysis
   2. Thyroid gland
   3. Inner ear
   4. Lower respiratory tract

57. **The dorsal mesentery of the primitive gut gives rise to the:**
   1. Falciform ligament
   2. Lienorenal ligament
   3. Lesser omentum
   4. Greater omentum

58. **Derived from mesonephric duct:**
   1. Uterine tube
   2. Seminiferous tubules
   3. Round ligament of uterus
   4. Ductus deferens

59. **Derived from ureteric bud:**
   1. Major calyces
   2. Minor calyces
   3. Collecting ducts
   4. Nephrons

60. **Derived from neural crest:**
   1. Spinal ganglia
   2. Neural tube
   3. Melanocytes
   4. Ventral horn cells

61. **Remnant(s) of embryonic thyroid outgrowth from the pharynx:**
   1. Branchial cyst
   2. Laryngocoele
   3. Cystic hygroma
   4. Pyramidal lobe

62. **Derived from second branchial arch:**
    1. Muscles of mastication
    2. Muscles of facial expression
    3. Ramus of mandible
    4. Styloid process of temporal bone

63. **Glial cells of ectodermal origin:**
    1. Ependymal cells
    2. Astrocytes
    3. Oligodendrocytes
    4. Microglia

Questions 64–78

The group of questions below consists of numbered headings, followed by a list of lettered words or phrases. For each heading select the *one* word or phrase which is most closely related to it. *Note:* Each choice may be used *only once.*

64.	Ventral mesogastrium	A	Ligamentum teres
65.	Dorsal mesogastrium	B	Falciform ligament
66.	Primitive dorsal	C	Greater omentum
	mesentery	D	Lateral umbilical
67.	Umbilical artery		ligament
68.	Umbilical vein	E	Sigmoid mesocolon

69.	Vitelline duct	A	Uterine tube
70.	Mesonephric duct	B	Ureter
71.	Paramesonephric duct	C	Urachus
72.	Metanephric duct	D	Meckel's diverticulum
73.	Allantois	E	Vas deferens

74.	Soft palate	A	Maxillary process
75.	Masseter	B	Mandibular arch
76.	External acoustic	C	First pharyngeal cleft
	meatus	D	First pharyngeal pouch
77.	Tympanic cavity	E	Hyoid arch
78.	Orbicularis oris		

Questions 79–93

In reply to the following questions indicate whether you think each statement is *True* or *False*:

In the developing heart:
79. The sinus venosus contributes to the formation of both atria
80. Most of the left atrium is formed from primitive pulmonary veins
81. Blood pressure is higher in the right atrium than in the left
82. A left-to-right shunt occurs through the foramen ovale
83. Deoxygenated blood from the right atrium passes mainly into the right ventricle

The 'physiological umbilical hernia' of the fetus:
84. Contains the fetal stomach
85. Occurs during the middle three months of gestation
86. Is reduced as the level of the diaphragm rises within the abdomen
87. Is inconstant
88. May persist until birth, as an abnormality

In the developing limb
89. Mitoses are scarce in the apical ectodermal ridge (crest)
90. Removal of the apical ridge causes cessation of limb growth
91. Most of the limb muscles develop *in situ*
92. Cell degeneration is important in development of the digits
93. Ossification of the carpus begins before birth

Embryo in utero

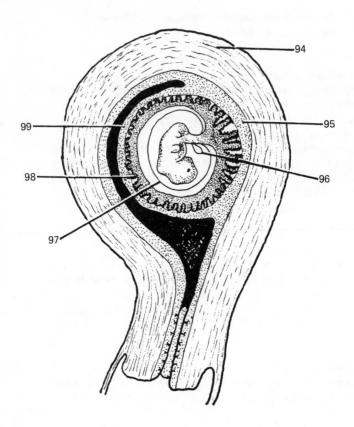

Identify the numbered structures, from the choices given below:

A   Chorion laeve   E   Decidua basalis
B   Chorion frondosum   F   Myometrium
C   Decidua capsularis   G   Decidua parietalis
D   Amnion   H   Yolk sac remnant

Sagittal section of embryo

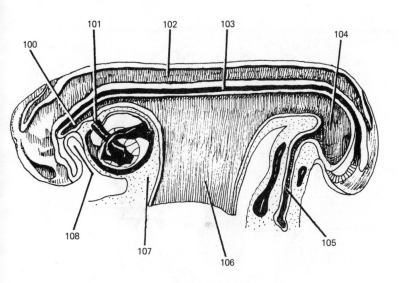

Identify the numbered structures, from the choices given below:

A	Notochord	F	Foregut
B	Septum transversum	G	Midgut
C	Neural tube	H	Truncus arteriosus
D	Cloaca	J	Stomodeum
E	Allantois	K	Vitelline duct

Section of embryo

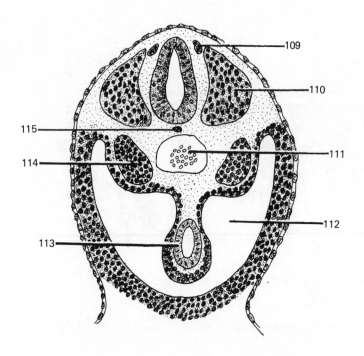

Identify the numbered structures, from the choices given below:

A   Neural crest
B   Notochord
C   Skin ectoderm
D   Aorta
E   Intermediate
    mesoderm

F   Gut
G   Sinus venosus
H   Paraxial mesoderm
J   Coelom
K   Extraembryonic
    mesoderm

Early placenta

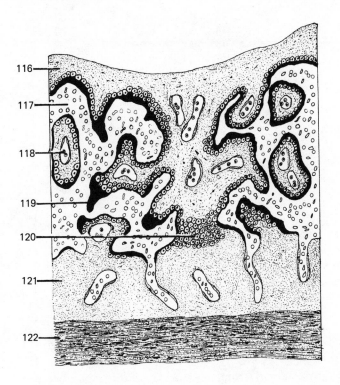

116
117
118
119
120
121
122

Identify the numbered structures, from the choices given below:

A	Amnion	F	Allantois
B	Extraembryonic mesoderm	G	Intervillous space
		H	Cytotrophoblast
C	Syncytiotrophoblast	J	Placental barrier
D	Fetal capillary	K	Decidua basalis
E	Myometrium		

Answers

1.	A	43.	B	83.	T	
2.	C	44.	A	84.	F	
3.	C	45.	B	85.	F	
4.	C	46.	B	86.	F	
5.	C			87.	F	
6.	C	47.	C	88.	T	
7.	A	48.	B	89.	T	
8.	B	49.	B	90.	T	
9.	B	50.	A	91.	T	
10.	B	51.	C	92.	T	
11.	C	52.	B	93.	F	
12.	B	53.	B			
13.	A	54.	C	94.	F	
14.	B	55.	B	95.	E	
15.	A	56.	C	96.	H	
16.	D	57.	C	97.	D	
17.	E	58.	D	98.	A	
18.	A	59.	A	99.	C	
19.	A	60.	B			
20.	D	61.	D	100.	F	
21.	A	62.	C	101.	H	
22.	A	63.	A	102.	C	
23.	A			103.	A	
24.	D	64.	B	104.	D	
25.	B	65.	C	105.	E	
26.	E	66.	E	106.	K	
27.	D	67.	D	107.	B	
28.	C	68.	A	108.	J	
29.	E	69.	D			
30.	C	70.	E	109.	A	
31.	A	71.	A	110.	H	
32.	E	72.	B	111.	D	
33.	A	73.	C	112.	J	
34.	C	74.	A	113.	F	
35.	D	75.	B	114.	E	
36.	A	76.	C	115.	B	
37.	D	77.	D			
		78.	E	116.	B	
38.	A			117.	G	
39.	A	79.	F	118.	D	
40.	B	80.	T	119.	C	
41.	D	81.	T	120.	H	
42.	A	82.	F	121.	K	
				122.	D